IMAGERY
AND
DISEASE

IMAGERY AND DISEASE

IMAGE-CA
IMAGE-SP
IMAGE-DB

A Diagnostic Tool for Behavioral Medicine

Jeanne Achterberg/G. Frank Lawlis

INSTITUTE FOR PERSONALITY AND ABILITY TESTING
CHAMPAIGN, ILLINOIS

Library of Congress Cataloging in Publication Data

Achterberg, Jeanne.
    Imagery and disease.

    Includes bibliographies and indexes.
    1. Medicine and psychology. 2. Imagery (Psychology)
3. Cancer--Psychosomatic aspects. 4. Backache--Psycho-
somatic aspects. 5. Diabetes--Psychosomatic aspects.
I. Lawlis, G. Frank. II. Title. [DNLM: 1. Behavioral
Medicine--instrumentation. 2. Diabetes Mellitus--
psychology. 3. Neoplasms--psychology. 4. Pain--
psychology. 5. Projective Technics-instrumentation.
6. Spinal Diseases--psychology. WM 145 A179i]
R726.A235 1984   616.07'5   84-22438
ISBN 0-918296-17-X

Institute for Personality and Ability Testing, Inc.
P.O. Box 188, Champaign, Illinois 61820

Printed in the United States of America.

Production Editor: Mary T. Russell; Cover by Peggy Cler

ACKNOWLEDGMENTS

The *Imagery of Cancer* was developed during a metamorphosis in both of our lives, and in some sense we regard it as the creative product of that profound change. During the year the data were collected and analyzed, we met and, recognizing our mutual archetypes, fell in love and married. We would like to dedicate the book first and foremost to our eternal relationship.

We are extremely grateful for the professional support received over the past eight years; this support allowed us to venture far afield from traditional psychology and medicine, yet kept us grounded within the mainstream of both disciplines. When our work in this area first began, Dr. Carl Simonton and Stephanie Mathews-Simonton permitted us to study their fine patients. In 1976, Dr. Phala Helm and Dr. Fred Cromes, in conjunction with the Cancer Rehabilitation Project at Southwestern Medical School, gave us a rich opportunity to substantiate our intuitions. Later, our faculty appointments in the Department of Physical Medicine were extremely valuable. We were placed in contact with medicine's finest researchers, were able to study the most serious diseases and disabilities known to humankind, and received generous grant support—surely the best of all worlds.

The current extension of the original *Imagery of Cancer* was made possible, in the first instance, by a most remarkable, rapid change in the *Zeitgeist*. Less than a decade ago, analyzing imagery to predict the course of physical disease was clearly bizarre. We anxiously awaited the replications, but had little hope that anyone else would have the energy to invest in this most difficult work, or even that clinicians would learn and use the test itself. We had underestimated the hunger for the understanding of the psyche's relationship to physical disease. Clinical validation came from contacts around the world. Not only was our work replicated, but extended in several directions. Most notably, Robert

Trestman's studies offered new insights, alternative scoring systems, and a refined analysis. His work is summarized here with his permission and that of Dr. Howard Pollio, chairperson of Trestman's dissertation committee at the University of Tennessee. The serious scholar will want to read the dissertation in its entirety—no summary could begin to do this massive undertaking justice.

The newest generation of researchers has begun to answer the most controversial, exciting question of all: Is the imagery causal or only reflective of physical change? In that regard, we wish to thank Drs. John Schneider, Wayne Smith, and their colleagues for permission to include their work here. As they carefully test the relationship of imagery to the control of the immune system (which is a prerequisite for influencing the course of cancer), they have reached out into the next dimension of science and medicine.

The Image-SP (Spinal Pain) is the result of a long-term collaborative effort among two of the finest orthopedic surgeons in the country, Dr. Vert Mooney and Dr. David Selby, together with Drs. C. E. McCoy and Frank Lawlis. They used, researched, and revised the pain drawing in the Spinal Pain Clinics at Parkland Hospital and Dallas Rehabilitation Institute, in their private practices, and (earlier, by Dr. Mooney) at Rancho Los Amigos rehabilitation facility. This work led to the Image-SP in its current form.

Acknowledgment for work on the Image-DB (Diabetes) is made to Dr. Larry Stevens, who not only validated the scoring system, but also conducted an experimental test of the effects of imagery on blood glucose levels.

A special thanks is given to Drs. Joel Robert Butler and Bz Cobb for their enduring friendship and the sustenance of their emotional and professional support. And finally, we should like to express our deep appreciation to Sam Krug, Karen Cattell, Gary Behrens, and Mary Russell at IPAT. Their support has been noteworthy, particularly as it became apparent to these publishers of psychological tests that only on the surface was the imagery analysis a test. Its foundation was a philosophical statement about the human spirit.

CONTENTS

TABLES

FIGURES

PART

I

IMAGE-CA

CHAPTER 1

INTRODUCTION

Like most terminal diseases, intimate contact with cancer spurs the scientist to discover its cause and cure. That being beyond the present realm of possibility, a reasonable understanding of the ways in which cancer patients deal with the disease in a constructive fashion can be pursued in order to aid in the medical treatment. As students of the body, we began to ask questions about the role patients play in their prognosis and treatment. Is the patient simply a mosaic of organs, and disease merely an obstacle to their functioning? Is it justifiable to view the physician or surgeon as a mechanic modifying or adapting the motor to regain functioning and the patient as passive and helpless with respect to both the doctor and disease?

From a broad and extensive review of the literature, we found abundant evidence to suggest that both quality and quantity of life measures were predicted by psychological dimensions, even to the extent of formulating hypotheses regarding premorbid variance and remediation in cancer. Rather than becoming entangled in a web of conjecture of impossible methodologies, we set out to determine what the patients themselves could tell us about their own understanding of what was happening to them and then to determine the accuracy of their prognoses. We formulated two specific goals in the research plan: (1) to understand cancer patients from a holistic perspective to the extent that we could explain not only behaviors in general, but how they behaved toward the disease as well, and (2) to formalize this understanding in order to enable other health professionals to reach the most effective level of communication with the cancer patient.

Our first task was to find out what "language" to use in communicating with the patients and their disease. We found that through a relaxation exercise they could focus and imagine aspects of their disease. By instructing them to draw these images, and through a structured interview, we began to recognize 14 scorable dimensions for standardization and quantification. These were vividness, activity, and strength of the cancer cell, vividness and activity of the white blood cell, relative comparison of size and numbers of cancer and white blood cells, strength of white blood cell, vividness and effectiveness of medical treatment, degree of symbolism, overall strength of imagery, regularity of imagery process, and clinical opinion related to prognosis based on combined imagery factors.

The instrument itself was developed after several hundred hours of patient sessions—listening and questioning them on the manner in which they perceived their disease, immunity, and treatment. Over the course of time, the 14 dimensions stood out remarkably well as key aspects in the disease imagery. Our intuitions regarding the relationship between the dimensions and the disease were verified when we were able to relate the scores to follow-up criteria.

The first group of patients that we studied provided incredibly valuable insights. They were all well educated, highly verbal, and for the most part intimately familiar with relaxation, meditation, and imagery techniques. Many were physicians, psychologists, biologists, and in allied health fields, so that their own professional backgrounds enhanced their discussion beautifully. To them we owe a significant debt of gratitude, and an acknowledgment that they are truly educators in the disease process.

Our concern that the relationship between imagery and disease course might have been unique only to an elite group of psychologically oriented patients was dispelled when we applied the IMAGE-CA to county hospital patients, most of whom were indigent, poorly educated, and scarcely familiar with such things as the phagocytic activity of the white blood cells. When this latter group was instructed to become physically relaxed and quiet, and to take an imaginary trip through their bodies, their perceptions proved to be valid prognosticators. These findings should serve to elevate cancer patients to new positions of personal responsibility and authority in disease management.

Fifty-eight cancer patients were used in the first validation study (Normative Group I) with disease status serving as a criterion. The predictive validity as well as concurrent validity of the instrument was upheld. A group of 22 lower class patients (Normative Group II) was the focus of the second effort. With this more homogeneous sample, functionability of the patients was the criterion. Both studies were consistent in reliability analyses and agreement checks. In both cases psychological and neurophysiological measures were correlated with the 14 dimensions in order to understand their relationships to other approaches. In a separate study with the technique (Achterberg, Lawlis, Simonton, & Simonton, 1977), it was found that psychological measures, especially the imagery dimensions, predicted disease progress much more accurately than blood chemistries.

Through our studies with the imagery technique and cancer patients, we feel that we have personally reached our first goal: to understand the cancer patient in a broader perspective. We can now predict from a variety of measurements the patients' expectancies and attitudes toward disease and treatment factors. We can more clearly understand the struggle for life. However, our goals also included helping others understand the cancer patients in confrontation with this dread disease. Consequently, we have attempted to formulate a specific approach designed to acquaint health professionals with methods that foster an understanding of patients and the role patients play in their own treatment. This book offers a systematic means of inviting patients' perceptions for hypothesis testing, in the same sense that physical data from the patients are obtained.

IMAGERY: A FOUNDATION FOR BEHAVIORAL MEDICINE

The notion of mental imagery, visualization, seeing with the mind's eye, or inner vision (or whatever one chooses

3

to call the introspective process that is accompanied by sensory images) has an extraordinarily rich history in both psychology and medicine. In fact, it formed the basis for study in the first psychological laboratory established by Wundt in 1879. The scientific analysis of the content of the mind seemed to be an appropriate area of research for the fledgling discipline, and psychologists began to try to objectify the nebulous arena of the imagination. Because the early results were neither pragmatic nor interpretable, psychologists turned to the analysis of behavior as their focus, dismissing the more phenomenological aspects once again as grist for the theologians and philosophers.

At the same time that experimentalists were turning their attentions elsewhere, psychologists engaged in therapy were discovering and refining the various facets of imagery as a treatment modality. Imagery, after all, is the stuff that dreams are made of: it is a facilitator of memory, an integral part of creativity, and may well be a prerequisite for attitude change. The recapturing of mental images, a process which allows a patient to work through long-repressed conflict, lies at the heart of traditional Freudian analysis. Jung, too, believed that the trip through the unconscious via visualization techniques produced a wealth of insight, offering the patient a means of dealing more effectively with life situations. He also held that this procedure was capable of enhancing emotional growth and of leading to an understanding of the more ethereal, mystical qualities of human existence.

Uncountable new modes of psychotherapy rely heavily or exclusively on the manipulation of the visualization procedure. To refer to them as new, however, is somewhat misleading, since they are largely innovations based on methods that can be traced to early Egyptians, to Shaman rituals from many cultures, and to classical hypnosis as well. These schools of therapy include Psychosynthesis, Gestalt, and Arica, to mention but a few, and generally involve the achievement of some relaxed or altered state of consciousness, followed by suggestions of either concrete images or of spontaneous imagery with the purpose varying from attitude change to physiologic alteration. Regardless of the procedure, the message is essentially the same: Image the type of person you wish to become, both in terms of mental and physiological factors, and through that process you will be more likely to reach your goals.

Scientific Analysis of Imagery

The renewed study of inner processes was recognized in 1964 by Robert Holt in an article in the *American Psychologist* entitled, "Imagery: The Return of the Ostracized." Imagery or visualization was welcomed back as an important area of scientific pursuit. Ironically, creative imagery has crept back into scientific psychology through a recognition of the basis for biofeedback procedures and counter-conditioning, both being practical applications of traditional learning theory. In the case of biofeedback, patients usually report some form of mental imagery that accompanies a change in autonomic function. Counter-conditioning stresses practice in visualizing a feared or noxious stimulus while in a relaxed physiological state. This latter therapy, particularly, acknowledges the delicate interplay between psyche and soma that is encouraged by the visualization technique.

In another context, Luria (1968) writing on eidectic imagery, has provided valuable information on the role of imagery in the learning-memory process. He and others have found that eidetic (or photographic) memory is not only an underlying phenomena of the learning process, but tends to diminish with age. Evidently the process of visual imagery or the storage of visual memories is in part replaced by verbal memory storage. We can probably safely assume that the ability to form visual images is normally distributed in the population and therefore does not remain the province of the few who exhibit pronounced photographic memory.

Neisser (1972), in discussing the difference between visualization and perception, claimed that the same kind of synthesis is involved in both, but in the case of visualization it is based on stored rather than on current incoming information. This view suggests that with the exception of the external input, the process of imagery involves the neurological substrates integral to the visual process itself.

5

The ability to form visual images has been examined by several investigators and found to correlate with psychological traits and abilities. Among those traits where a positive correlation exists are hypnotic susceptibility (Palmer & Field, 1968; Wagman & Stewart, 1974), ease of verbal learning (Paivio, 1969), personality characteristics of intro-version/extraversion (Huckabee, 1974), confusion in consciousness (Richardson, 1969; Sheehan, 1973), and creative self-perceptions (Khatina, 1975).

Despite widespread interest, the measurement of the imagery experience, per se, remains a complex impediment to the understanding of the process since it consists of intrinsically private events which have remained externally unverifiable. Such complications are not new to psychology, however, since the "core" areas of the discipline such as learning, motivation, and perception have also been fraught with all the problems of the verification of hypothetical constructs.

While the ability to image and vividness of imagery have been fairly well studied in regard to relationships with certain events, the actual content of the imagery seems to have been neglected from an analytical viewpoint except in clinical report (e.g., Cautela, 1975). Yet the imagery content would seem to be most necessarily correlated with the outcome of the procedure. It is not merely the capability of the individual to image, but the nature of the image itself that eventuates in any change in attitude, perceptual, or physiological function.

Physiological Correlates of Imagery

Several studies have demonstrated that when the appropriate neuronal pathways are artificially stimulated by some means, images are experienced. For example, neither during dream sleep, nor during hallucinations, nor when visual pathways of the brain are electrically stimulated is the retina actually involved. We are forced to conclude that the fine line between external and internal visual reality is simply a matter of peripheral vs. no-peripheral stimulation. Images are "real" to the person experiencing them, and presumably because they share common neurological pathways with the externally produced images, they are capable of evoking the same physiological or psychological response.

Jacobsen's work (1942) has had a pronounced effect on our understanding of the physiological ramifications of mental imagery. His research indicated that during imagery there is measurable tension in the part of the body involved in the visualization. For example, there is tension in the muscles of the eye during visual imagery, in the muscles of speech during sub-vocal thought, and in leg muscles when one imagines running. This tension merely reflects the involvement of conscious control over voluntary muscle groups and is, therefore, certainly no mystery. However, this consequence of mental imagery has led writers to propose advantages to mentally imaging or rehearsing physical feats prior to their exhibition (tennis players, golfers, and basketball players as well as others have professed to using some form of imagery).

Luria (1968) has also described the relationship of mental imagery to physiological response. He reported on a most unusual patient, adept at eidetic imagery, who was able to increase his heart rate significantly by imagining himself running to catch a train, and could decrease his heart rate back to normal by imaging himself in bed trying to go to sleep. In another experiment the subject was able to differentially raise the temperature of one hand by imaging his hand on a hot stove; again to decrease the temperature by seeing himself squeeze a piece of ice. His amazing subject was also able to alter pupil size by visualizing light, and could likewise influence the cochlear reflex by imaging a sudden sound. Admittedly, Luria was working with an exceptional patient, but as is the case with most advances, we learn by studying the anomalies.

The physiological effects of the mental imagery process has been documented by Drs. Schultz and Luthe (1969) in their compilation of 2400 studies based on the use of autogenic therapy. This therapeutic technique involves the use of visualization and relaxation procedures, offered in a highly structured framework. Changes accompanying the procedures often include alterations in temperature, blood sugar, blood pressure, white blood cell count, and brain wave

7

patterns. However, many of these changes occur naturally by relaxation alone. Therefore the relationship between visualization and relaxation and the relative contribution of each to the end result is still unclear.

The achievement of physical relaxation seems to greatly enhance the production of visual images (Richardson, 1969). Therefore, in a therapeutic context, relaxation techniques usually serve as a prelude to imagery suggestions. Total relaxation seems to be required in order for a patient to focus internally, to obliterate the demands made on the central nervous system by the maintenance and experience of muscular tension, and to gate out diversionary external stimuli. The ability to achieve a relaxed state also involves imagery to some extent, however. The patients usually imagine tension in some way flowing out of the body; they see muscles changing in their form and state, the body warming via some internal production of heat. On another level, Benson (1975) and his colleagues have identified a series of physiological responses associated with simple relaxation. These responses can be thought of as conducive to a reestablishment of the body's equilibrium or homeostasis. They include lowered blood pressures, increased blood flow, decreased heart rate, intensification of alpha response, and a general decrease in metabolic processes indicated by decreased oxygen consumption and carbon dioxide production as well as a decrease in respiration. Benson calls the conglomerate response a wakeful, hypometabolic state which indicates the organism is mentally alert, but physically exhibits decreased sympathetic nervous system activity.

Imagery in Medicine

In view of the wide range of physical events that have been correlated with the production of visual imagery, a relationship between images and the healing or disease process logically follows. The use of visualization to promote healing may well have been the first form of the practice of medicine, and may also influence the effectiveness of any medical procedure. It stands to reason that in antiquity imagery would have been used to combat disease. Sickness, like any other unexplained event, was attributed to malevolent, unseen spirits. Quite logically, thought forms were then used to combat thought forms. Historical records from Babylonia, Assyria, Summaria, and Greece describe elaborate rituals for ridding the body of disease. Most of these ancient cultures relied on a practitioner skilled in the arts of imagination to guide the afflicted person through thoughts, dreams, or appeals to the gods to effect a healing. Many of these same procedures are currently being practiced by Indian tribes, particularly the Navaho and Canadian Eskimo tribes. Trance-inducing ceremonies which are intended to assist Shamans with diagnostic insight are performed, after which they apply the tools of their trade (herbs, sand painting, laying on of hands, songs, chants, and disease extraction). We heartily recommend Samuels & Samuels' *Seeing with the Mind's Eye*, 1975, for a graphic presentation of these and other imagery materials.

It has only been a recent development that medicine or healing is considered a separate discipline. For centuries, it was a free-for-all, with contributory statements made by virtually every philosophical and religious group concerned with human nature. Interestingly, the use of imagery as a tool for retaining or regaining health is found in Christian doctrine, Buddhism, Hinduism, in the Kaballist tradition of Judaism, Hermetic and Palatonic philosophy, and in Rosicrucianism. In all of these, the functions of the mind have supremacy over the physical attributes which are believed to be only the concretion or manifestation of the former.

Now, physicians and other professionals closely allied with the medical profession have developed alternative methods of healing based upon the systematic use of the imagination. Drs. Irving Oyle and Mike Samuels widely employ imagery in the general practice of medicine. Grantly Dick-Read pioneered new methods of childbirth using imagery to alleviate fear and pain. Carl Simonton, Bernard Siegel, Bernaur Newton, and scores of others use imagery in some form with cancer patients. Dean Olnish and Joe D. Goldstrich have incorporated imagery into cardiac rehabilitation settings. The efficacy of imagery techniques used by these professionals has not been subjected to experimental test. Nevertheless, support for its use can be extrapolated from the findings of experimental psychologists, physiologists, biochemists, and personality theorists who have investigated the involvement of mental factors in disease.

The immediate predecessor to the modern use of the imagination is the autogenic therapy procedure developed by W. Schultz in the 1930s (Luthe, 1969). This complicated series of exercises involves imagining a heaviness in the extremities and peaceful scenes, concentrating on feelings of warmth, and attaining mental contact with vital organs. The patient is instructed in specific visualizations including spontaneously imaged colors, objects, concepts, and feelings. Visualization prescriptions are used in treating many conditions including ulcers, colitis, heart disease, obesity, and diabetes.

Although Schultz and Luthe and others refer to their practices as "visualization," and use the word interchangeably with imagery, this seems to be a semantic oversight not born out in their actual work. In its typical medical usage, imagery is not restricted to the sense of vision alone.[1] Visualizations are commonly reported, but any sensory modality may be involved, including audition, smell, and even kinesthesis. Images associated with the greatest physical changes vividly encompass the gamut of the senses. Another phenomenon that is frequently reported as being associated with the imagery procedure is a feeling state such as tingling, warmth, or movement within the area being focused upon. Occasionally, these feelings are the *only* sensory processes reported. (It would be of great interest to identify the physiological correlates of these feelings to determine whether or what healing mechanisms might be involved.)

From the earliest records of medicine, the imagination has been used by both the healer and the patient in two fundamental tasks: diagnosis and therapy. Indeed, most of the world's medical information has come through the imagination, manifested in dreams and visions. Does empirical test support the most ancient of all healing traditions? The Image-CA was created in response to that question and specifically concerns the role of the imagination in diagnosis.

[1]In the first edition of this book, we sometimes referred to visualization and visual imagery when we were referring to imagery that could involve other senses as well as the visual. On reprinting, the publisher did not change all of these "visualization" references to "imagery" references because of the prohibitive costs involved. However, readers would do well to remember as they read that imagery is not limited to the visual sense alone.

The Image-CA was developed after 20 months of testing, interviewing, and observing cancer patients as they participated in group therapy sessions with the Simontons. These highly articulate, well-educated patients had remarkable stories to tell about their struggle for life. They could describe in extensive detail their motivations, their disappointments, and the events leading up to the diagnosis of their disease. Furthermore, they had inner pictures of the disease and of forces within themselves that could combat the proliferating cells.

Because the Simonton patients were used initially to gain insight into the human condition (and nowhere could one find more insightful people), the development and use of the Image-CA has been frequently misunderstood. Never has the use of the imagination been relegated to a chosen few. Neither social class nor race nor awareness of medical information precludes vivid, complex imagery associated with a diagnosis of cancer, although these factors may well shape the form the images take and alter their interpretation. The imagery findings were subsequently validated on a diverse group of cancer patients, many of them indigent and dependent upon government resources for their basic needs. Others were veterans who had a longstanding history of alcoholism. Very, very few of the patients studied (with the exception of the Simonton group) would have considered using imagery, or any meditation other than familiar prayers, much less going to a psychotherapist to gain help with their disease.

Each cancer patient has images of his or her condition. And, like it or not, all health professionals help create the substance of the imagery through their interactions, through their words, and even through what they leave unsaid. Imagery is the process involved in encouraging the will to live. It is the expectation transmitted to the patient regarding the imminence of their demise. The placebo effect, or what the patient believes will happen following medical treatment, directly influences the outcome of the disease itself. These events are inseparable from any medical practice.

There are two implications derived from the evidence that supports the power of the imagination to both kill and cure. (1) The images must relate to disease, either in terms of

11

reflecting the current condition, or as predictive of its future course. (2) The imagination can be regarded as a primary causal factor in the outcome of disease. Cancer, then, would be expected to be more influenced by the imagination than any other disease, given the prevailing cultural metaphor imbuing the diagnosis with the sentence of death. Since technology alone has not conquered the disease, the systematic measurement of the role of the imagination should no longer be avoided.

Linking Body and Mind: Scientific Support for the Imagination

The theoretical basis for the relationship between physical disease and the cognitive processes reflected in a patient's imagery are derived from three factors: (1) the surveillance theory of cancer development; (2) the distress associated with the development of disease; and (3) principles of biofeedback (Achterberg, Simonton, & Matthews-Simonton, 1976). According to the surveillance theory (Prehn, 1969), abnormal cells occur occasionally within an organism but are usually successfully attacked by the body's immune system which is a combination of factors primarily involving the white blood cells. Only rarely does this system break down and allow clinical malignancy to develop. The cancer cells, rather than being strong, are viewed as metabolically confused and vulnerable to the normal attacking properties of the white blood cells. Secondly, the literature on the relationship between stress and cancer as well as other diseases is quite conclusive: both psychological and physiological stress can lead to a breakdown in host resistance through alterations in hormonal levels and in related dysfunctions of the immune system components (Riley, 1975; Solomon & Amkraut, 1972). Finally, the work on biofeedback has led to an awareness of the ability to consciously control body functions that were previously thought of as autonomic. Heart rate, blood flow, gastric processes, temperature, and other functions have been shown in innumerable studies to be conditionable, with the crucial factor being the ability of the patient to monitor or observe these functions. So, taken together, these three factors strongly suggest that psychological processes can

12

interact with natural physical processes in the development of disease, and that, conversely, a patient can use these factors to gain control of physiological functioning.

The proposed mechanism for the interaction between psychological and physical factors is diagrammed in Figures 1 and 2. The model is derived principally from the work of Hans Selye (1956) and involves much of what is known about the physiological concomitants of stress. The emotions accompanying stress—fear, anxiety, and depression—are reflected in limbic system activity, which directly involves hypothalamic and pituitary function. The pituitary, the body's master gland, regulates all hormonal activity. Furthermore, imbalances in hormonal activity have frequently been demonstrated to be connected to increases in malignant growth. Oversecretion of the adrenal has been particularly noted to affect the thymus and lymph integrity and subsequently the white blood cells. Stress can thus be viewed as having a two-fold influence on the malignant process: (1) the production of abnormal cells increases, and (2) the capability of the body to destroy these cells is diminished.

Prior to 1980, the evidence supporting the contention that psychological processes are directly involved in the reversal of serious malignancy came largely from a vast accumulation of case reports and personal testimony. Profound happiness, deep faith, an intense preoccupation with living to fulfill a dream all have been noted repeatedly (perhaps by every observant clinician) to accompany remission. Yet, these same events have been dismissed by the established medical community as irrelevant for scientific scrutiny, even though they offer the only evidence for cure of the incurable. Since every thought is accompanied by electro-chemical change (thought *is* an electrochemical event), then it was only a matter of time before the chemicals of hope and joy and trust could be identified and their relationship to disease revealed.

Within the last few years, the study of immunology has taken on new dimensions which promise insight into the mysteries of cancer. Investigators from the Research Institute of Scripps Clinic have found that endorphins (the body's natural opiates) enhance the ability of T-cells to pro-

13

FIGURE 1

Psychophysiological Model of Cancer Growth

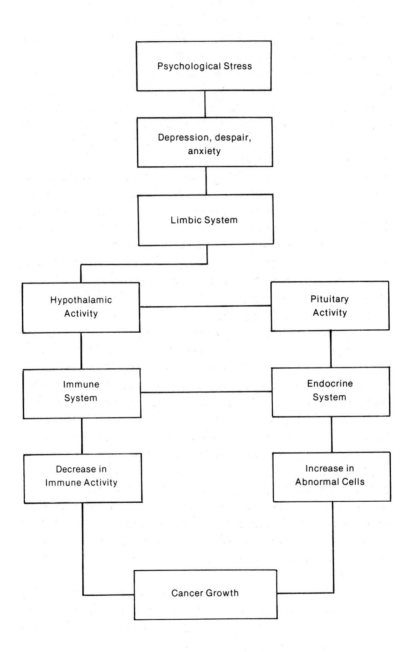

FIGURE 2

Psychophysiological Model of Cancer Regression

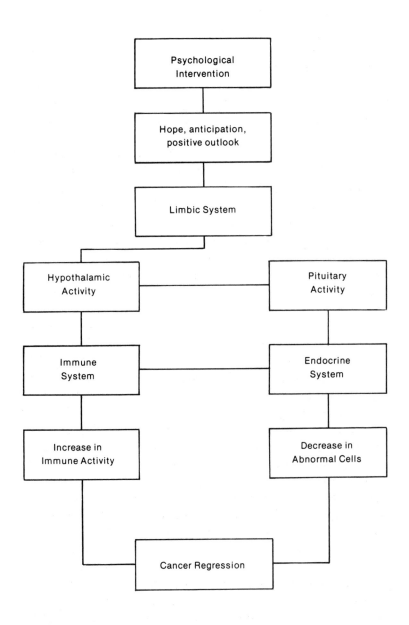

liferate (Gilman, et al., 1982). The T-cells are white blood cells specifically targeted for fighting cancer (as well as other diseases). The endorphins have been associated with states of euphoria and pain alleviation and therefore are likely candidates for the chemicals of remission. Other investigators suggest the endorphins may be "immunomodulators," in that they assist the immune system in fighting disease. The activity of T-cells taken from cancer patients was significantly enhanced through exposure to the endorphins (Plotnikoff, 1982).

A new discipline called "psychoneuroimmunology" has emerged, offering sound experimental evidence for the role of the brain in the immune response. Between 1976-1982 alone, Locke and Hornig-Rohan identified 1,300 studies in the professional literature and published the bibliography in a format titled *Mind and Immunity: Behavioral Immunology* (1983). Unfortunately, most of the work cited continues to focus on the deteriorative effects of stress-related circumstances; it's clearly easier to show how people make themselves sick rather than how they participate in their own healing process.

In a few instances, though, courageous, controversial, and exciting work is being reported that, if sufficiently replicated, must ultimately change the practice of medicine. The work has demonstrated that conscious manipulation of the immune system in a direction consonant with health is possible. The imagination is the link between the will to alter the response and the immunological changes. For instance, Howard Hall administered hypnosis—a form of imagery training—specifically designed to increase the activity of the T-cells (Hall, 1983; Hall, Longo, & Dixon, 1981). Barbara Peavey trained highly stressed, immunodeficient subjects to relax, using biofeedback together with a program of education and stress management, and then measured changes in neutrophils, a type of white blood cell (Peavey, 1983). John Schneider, Wayne Smith, and colleagues (1983) taught subjects to image various functions of neutrophils and observed subsequent changes in their blood. Positive, statistically significant effects on the immune system were noted in each of these well-controlled studies. From these results, it is reasonable to assert that the mind, particularly that aspect of mind we think of as the imagination, can exert a positive influence on immunology, and hence on cancer itself.

From a humanistic standpoint, it has never been tenable to consider cancer as a disease of cells, with tumors existing apart from their host. Scientific evidence now supports the need to view the disease in its broadest physical, mental, and even spiritual context. This poses a dilemma for most cancer research which has tended to become more reductionistic and obscure, with continued emphasis on the "witchcraft" concept, i.e., cancer as being caused by some unknown invasion from outside the individual. The futility of this approach is evidenced by the cancer statistics themselves: there is a steadily increasing incidence of cancer of most sites, and with the exception of childhood leukemia, uterine cancer, and a few other relatively rare disorders, the number of deaths from the disease has not significantly decreased, despite some prolongation of life.

Cancer and Psychological Processes

In preparing this section we have reviewed nearly 50 studies, dating back to 1839, which have examined the relationship between psychological processes and cancer. Rather than describing each of these studies, a summary of the instrumentation and psychological variables found to relate to malignancy is presented in Table 1.

There are two general conclusions that are evident from this research. First, regardless of instrumentation, there are enough replications to formalize the notion that a relationship does exist between the course of the disease and psychological dimensions. Second, several premorbid psychological factors consistently appear. For example, the memory of an early home life inadequate to needs of support and security, a pre-disease event of an emotional loss, and feelings described as helplessness or hopelessness all emerged in several independent investigations.

Although many of the studies utilized standardized psychological measurement, the instruments used were primarily developed for diagnosis of mental illness. Therefore, the conceptualizations involved may be inadequate or inappro-

Table 1

LITERATURE SUMMARY OF PSYCHOLOGICAL FACTORS RELATED TO CANCER

Author(s)	Year	Instrumentation	N	Psychological Factors Related to Cancer
Walshe	(1846)	observation	unknown	"woman of high color and sanguinous temperament"
Paget	(1870)	observation	unknown	deep anxiety, deferred hope and disappointment
Snow	(1883, 1890, 1893)	observation	250	depression
Evans	(1926)	psychotherapy progress	100	the last of a major catharsis
Foque	(1931)	observation	unknown	sad emotions
Miller & Jones	(1948)	observation	6	frequent occurrence of emotional difficulties
Bacon, Renneker, & Cutler	(1952)	case history	40	masochistic character inhibited sexuality and motherhood, inability to discharge anger
Greene	(1954, 1966)	interview	20	loss of significant other
Jacobs	(1954)	observation	unknown	self-destructiveness
Greene, Young, & Swisher	(1956)	observation	32	unresolved attachment to mother
Inman	(1964)	case study	1	guilt over masturbation
Muslin, Gyarfas, & Pieper	(1966)	questionnaires	74	separation from significant other
Greene	(1966)	observation	100	sadness, anxiety, anger, or hopelessness
Paloucek & Graham	(1966)	observation	88	psychosocial trauma and poor childhood
Kissen	(1967)	interview	930	disturbed relationships in childhood, ongoing adverse life situations
Blumberg	(1954)	MMPI, Rorschach	50	defensiveness, anxiety, low ability to reduce tension
Ellis & Blumberg	(1954)	case studies		low ability to reduce tension

Author		Instrument	N	Findings
Bugental	(1954)	MMPI (Blumberg's sample)		brooding, useless, lacking in energy
Wheeler & Caldwell	(1955)	Rorschach	60	labile, preoccupation with sexual body, inhibited with early sex experiences, close attachment with mother
LeShan & Worthington	(1956)	Worthington Personal History	152	loss of important relationship, inability to express hostility, anxiety over death
Kissen & Eysenck	(1962)	Maudsley Personal Inventory	116	extraversion, neuroticism
Coppen & Metcalfe	(1964)	Maudsley Personal Inventory	47	extraversion
Nemeth & Mezei	(1954)	Rorschach	50	few M, lower 4%, passive hostility
Booth	(1964)	Rorschach	93	rigid guilt feelings toward others
Evans, Stern, & Marmorston	(1965)	adjective checklist	56	submissiveness
Netzer	(1965)	Taylor Manifest Anxiety Scale Neuroticism Scale, DAP	50	body image distortions, denial, fear of loss of control, neuroticism
Kissen	(1966)	interview, MMPI	150	incidences of child behavior problems
Koenig, Levin, & Brennan	(1967)	MMPI	36	depression
Tarlau & Smalheiser	(1951)	interview, Rorschach, DAP	11	mother-child relationship
Cobb	(1952)	Rorschach, interview	100	anticipatory fears and underlying dependency
Reznikoff	(1955)	TAT, sentence completion	50	birth order and family domesticity, sadness, negative feelings
Bahnson & Bahnson	(1964b)	Rorschach	12	superficial extraversion, low empathy, "flattened" affect, rigid, constricted
LeShan	(1966)	Worthington Research Life History	450	early childhood relationship problems, recent adult event, loneliness
Bahnson & Bahnson	(1966)	interview	49	denial and repression of impulses
Achterberg & Lawlis	(1978)	Image-Ca, MMPI, Firo-B		denial, imagery, negative self-investment
Thomas	(1976)	questionnaire		early neglect

priate when applied to seriously ill patients, particularly if used to determine psychotherapeutic interventions. For this reason as well as others, the impact of psychological findings on the medical community has been slight. The jargon in psychological testing (such as "extraversion," "archetypes,") does little to facilitate interdisciplinary communication.

The heavy emphasis in the literature on attempting to define a cancer personality based on retrospective (post-diagnosis) information has not yielded much practical information for the health practitioner. In the first place, data gathered in this manner is of questionable validity; and secondly, premorbid psychological dimensions and events are not specific to present or future perspectives. There is very little one can do about past history or events that occur as a consequence of time. Clearly, in order to develop a better understanding of disease management, practitioners need new instrumentation specific to cancer and its psychological components. Therefore, the objectives for the design and construction of the IMAGE-CA were as follows:

1. *The instrument should form a closer communication link between physician and patient.* As medical training is intensified from year to year with more and more information available, the physician's learning becomes focused on the pathologies of organs and specific diagnosis, rather than on getting to know the patients. As the need for specialists grows, the patient becomes more a mosaic for referral sources than a personality.

This description is not intended as a criticism of medical training. There are logical reasons for these developments, such as the tremendous volume of medical information to learn and high caseloads. However, these factors have also placed the patients in a position of passivity, with little information about their condition.

2. *The instrument should assist the patient to participate in the rehabilitation process.* As a natural consequence of good communication with one's physician, the patients can more effectively aid their own remediation. As any physician will admit, medication or surgery can only assist the body in the

natural process. If the patient understands the intent of the medical treatment, two things tend to happen. He or she gains hope and self-confidence, and trust in the physician. The resultant positive attitude often contributes as much to health as anything else. There are numerous case studies which have demonstrated healthy responses once patients have gained the anticipatory reaction associated with hope.

Through research in biofeedback we know that people have the capacity to control a variety of bodily responses, provided a monitoring device is available. Moreover, research has shown that subjects can demonstrate autonomic control with selected imagery as well as, if not better than, with a biofeedback apparatus system.

Why couldn't patients be educated as to what autonomic systems need to be energized or slowed down, and be encouraged to image their recovery? Through control of thought processes a state of mind conducive to remediation could be developed at the very least, with the potential of significant healing at best.

3. *The instrument should allow the physician to anticipate the course of disease.* As affirmed by the research results, the course of cancer and probably other disease groups as well can be better predicted by psychological variables than medical measures (Achterberg, et al., 1977). This prediction is not surprising due to the fact that blood chemistries, blood pressure, and other physical measures are primarily reactive to disease state. Therefore, the physician using these measures is always predicting from a post hoc dimension. With the development of predictive measurement, the physician can provide treatment protocols for future disease complications as well as engaging psychological intervention methods, if needed.

CHAPTER 2
THE TECHNIQUE

The Imagery technique utilizes two media of communication which are of mutual importance: (1) a personalized drawing of the disease components, and (2) a structured interview. Specifically, the approach is to guide the patient through relaxation exercises and then through a focus on the disease process. There is a subtle educational process during which the patient is instructed to imagine the cancer cells, the immunological system represented by white blood cells, and any medical treatment in whatever way he or she wishes. After the patient is given the opportunity to actively image this process, he or she is asked to draw the images for the examiner. The interview is an attempt to clarify and objectify the meanings underlying the patient's drawings. The drawings and interview are then scored on the following 14 dimensions using 5-point scales:

1. Vividness of the cancer cell.
2. Activity of the cancer cell.
3. Strength of the cancer cell.
4. Vividness of the white blood cell.
5. Activity of the white blood cell.
6. Relative comparison of numbers of cancer cells to white blood cells.
7. Relative comparison of the size of cancer cells to white blood cells.
8. Strength of the white blood cell.
9. Vividness of the medical treatment (radiation, chemotherapy, surgery, etc.).

10. Effectiveness of the medical treatment.

11. Concreteness vs. symbolism.

12. Overall strength of imagery; emotional investment the patient projects to his drawing.

13. Estimated regularity of the number of times per day the patient thinks of his disease in the described way.

14. A clinical opinion by the examiner as to the prognosis for disease.

The 14 scale scores are then weighted and summed, yielding an overall Imagery Score. A more complete and detailed description of administration and scoring procedures follows.

ADMINISTRATION OF THE IMAGE-CA*

Information on which judgments are based for the IMAGE-CA consists of:

1. Drawings of (a) the cancer cell, or the disease
            (b) the immune system (usually referred to as white blood cells)
            (c) any treatment for the malignancy
   and
2. Dialogue which deals with the description and inter-action of the three categories listed above.

Materials required for administration and scoring are:

1. Tape recording, "Relaxation and Guided Imagery."

2. Drawing materials (8½ x 11" white sheets and repro-duction pencils).

3. IMAGE-CA Interview Record and Scoring Sheet.

The manner in which this information is collected is highly contingent upon the patient involved. The patient's

*For purchase of materials and audiotapes, contact the publisher.

NAME

IMAGE-CA
Interview Record and Scoring Sheet

Jeanne Achterberg and G. Frank Lawlis

Biographical/Treatment Data

Age _____   Sex _____   Marital Status _____

Type of Treatment: Date(s):

    Surgery   On _____

    Radiation   from _____ to _____

    Chemotherapy/Immunotherapy   from _____ to _____

    Other   from _____ to _____

Diagnosis: Primary Site _____

                                Secondary Site(s) _____

Current Disease Status: _____ 1) no evidence of disease

                                 _____ 2) disease stabilized

                               _____ 3) continued active disease

IMAGE-CA Total Score (sten) _____

DATE

Instructions

This booklet is designed for recording and scoring information obtained from patient imagery drawings. After the patient has listened to the guided relaxation exercise, instruct him/her to draw, on a separate 8½ x 11-inch sheet of white paper, (1) the white blood cells, (2) any treatment being received, and (3) the cancer cells, all acting inside the body. When the drawings are completed, begin the interview using pages 3 and 4.

Following the interview, score the imagery/interview content according to the 14 Dimensions appearing on page 2. After scoring each of these scales, fold in page 4 so that **IMAGE CA - Summary Data** (page 5) is directly opposite page 2. Transcribe the 14 scores in column (2) of the table provided on page 5. Next, multiply each of the individual scores by the weights appearing in column (3) and enter the product in column (4). Add these components and enter the sum in the appropriate box marked "Weighted Sum." Then, in the appropriate sten conversion table, find the interval containing the obtained weighted sum and the corresponding sten score.

INSTITUTE FOR PERSONALITY AND ABILITY TESTING, INC.

P. O. Box 188, Champaign, Illinois 61820

FIGURE 3

IMAGE-CA - Imagery Scoring Sheet

*Circle the number you feel best describes the imagery,
based on the information you have available.*

CANCER CELLS

	1	2	3	4	5
1. Vividness	1 very unclear	2 somewhat unclear	3 moderately vivid	4 quite vivid	5 maximumly vivid
2. Activity	1 very active	2 quite active	3 moderately active	4 somewhat active	5 not at all active
3. Strength	1 very strong	2 quite strong	3 moderately strong	4 moderately weak	5 quite weak

WHITE BLOOD CELLS (Immune System)

	1	2	3	4	5
4. Vividness	1 very unclear	2 somewhat unclear	3 moderately clear	4 quite vivid	5 maximumly vivid
5. Activity	1 not active	2 some activity	3 moderately active	4 quite active	5 very active
6. Numerosity (relative to Cancer Cells)	1 many more Ca than WBC	2 few more Ca than WBC	3 about the same WBC & Ca	4 few more WBC	5 many more WBC than Ca
7. Size (relative to Cancer Cells) ...	1 Ca much larger than WBC	2 Ca somewhat larger	3 Ca and WBC about same	4 WBC little larger	5 WBC much larger than Ca
8. Strength	1 quite weak	2 moderately weak	3 somewhat strong	4 quite strong	5 very strong

TREATMENT (Circle "3" if patient is not receiving treatment)

	1	2	3	4	5
9. Vividness	1 very unclear, confused	2 somewhat unclear	3 moderately clear	4 quite vivid	5 very vivid, clear
10. Effectiveness	1 not at all effective	2 moderately ineffective	3 moderately effective	4 quite effective	5 highly effective

GENERAL

	1	2	3	4	5
11. How Symbolistic is visualization vs. How Concrete	1 very factual, concrete	2 moderately factual, concrete	3 mixed symbolistic/factual	4 moderately symbolistic	5 highly symbolistic
12. Overall Strength of Imagery vs. Weakness	1 very weak	2 quite weak	3 moderate	4 quite strong	5 very sound, strong
13. Estimated regularity	1 not imaging	2 infrequent	3 moderately regular	4 high level of consistency	5 extremely frequent
14. In your opinion, how is this type of imagery related to short-term disease management	1 continued active disease	2 some stabilization	3 considerable stabilization	4 eventual remission	5 rapid remission

FIGURE 3 (Continued)

IMAGE-CA - Interview Record

Cancer

1. Describe how your cancer cells look in your mind's eye.

2. Do you see the cancer cells moving around? If so, how? When?

3. How strong (tough) do you think your cells are? (Score on strength described or imputed to symbol chosen).

White Blood Cells [WBC]

4. Describe your WBC. (Score on vividness, clarity, continuity of description).

5. Do you see your WBC moving? If so, how? Where? (Score on activity or potential activity of symbol).

6. Do you see more cancer or more WBC? (Scoring on obvious response).

FIGURE 3 (Continued)

7. How big are your cancer cells? Your white blood cells?* (Score on relative difference with "5" indicating WBC significantly larger).

8. *How* do the WBC fight disease in your body? How well do you see the WBC as doing their job? (Score on strength or effectiveness).

Treatment

9. How does your treatment work to rid your body of disease? (Score on clarity and vividness).

10. How *well* does your treatment work to kill off disease? (Score on effectiveness described).

Miscellaneous Response

11. (Score on symbolism vs. concretion).

12. (Score on weak vs. strong).

13. How many times a day do you think about (or image) your cancer? (Record response).

14. (Score imagery on basis of how you would predict it related to disease from a clinical standpoint, i.e., "5" would indicate it predicted complete recovery, a "1" would predict a poor prognosis or death).

---

*Patient may be confused on difference between cancer *cell* and *tumor*. If so, some explanation or rewording may be required.

FIGURE 3 (Continued)

IMAGE-CA - Summary Data *

(1)	(2)	(3)	(4)
			Weighted
Dimension	Score	x Weight =	Score
1	_____	x 1	_____
2	_____	x 1	_____
3	_____	x 3	_____
4	_____	x 3	_____
5	_____	x 4	_____
6	_____	x 1	_____
7	_____	x 3	_____
8	_____	x 4	_____
9	_____	x 2	_____
10	_____	x 3	_____
11	_____	x 1	_____
12	_____	x 6	_____
13	_____	x 1	_____
14	_____	x 16	_____

➡ ☐ Weighted Sum Without Dimension 14 (see Columns 5a and 6a below)

➡ ☐ Weighted Sum With Dimension 14 (see Columns 5b and 6b below)

Sten Conversion Table
For Use With Only 13 Dimensions
(omitting clinical judgment, Dimension 14)

(5a) Weighted Sum	(6a) Sten	
165 or greater	10	Excellent imagery
153-162	9	
144-152	8	Good imagery
134-143	7	
125-133	6	Average imagery
115-124	5	
106-114	4	Less than average
96-105	3	imagery
87- 95	2	Poor imagery
less than 86	1	

Sten Conversion Table
For Use With All 14 Dimensions

(5b) Weighted Sum	(6b) Sten	
247 or greater	10	Excellent imagery
229-246	9	
213-228	8	Good imagery
195-212	7	
178-194	6	Average imagery
161-177	5	
144-160	4	Less than average
127-143	3	imagery
110-126	2	Poor imagery
less than 109	1	

---

* Note: For individuals with relatively little experience using the IMAGE-CA drawing technique (less than 50 administrations), omission of Dimension 14 is advised. Therefore, the sten conversion table on the left of this page should be used. For a more detailed explanation of scoring procedures, see pp. 85-89, *Imagery of Cancer: An evaluation tool for the process of disease,* Achterberg & Lawlis, 1978.

FIGURE 3 (Continued)

physical condition is of primary consideration. The manner of administration will differ greatly depending upon whether a patient is ambulatory or bedridden, highly medicated or alert, inpatient or outpatient, and so forth. We encountered patients at every conceivable stage of disease, socioeconomic level, and motivational state. The variables involved in a patient's willingness and ability to perform must be dealt with on an individual basis. The usual format for administration will be given below and includes (1) listening to a relaxation and guided imagery tape, (2) drawing the visualizations, and (3) a structured interview. Under no circumstances should testing take place before a close rapport is established.

Relaxation and Guided Imagery Instructions

All patients on whom IMAGE-CA was developed had some exposure to an audio tape recording which began with relaxation exercises, and was followed by information on imaging the cancer, the immune system, and any treatment that was being administered. One group of patients (Normative Group I) had listened to a tape produced by Carl Simonton (Special recording, Cognetics, Inc.) three times daily for a minimum of two weeks prior to their first session. The Medical School/county hospital patients (Normative Group II) were exposed to another audio tape only once immediately prior to administration of the IMAGE-CA. A transcript of this tape, developed primarily for this evaluation instrument follows:

Transcription of the Cancer Evaluation Tape

This is a tape that will help you relax your body and understand your disease a little better. First of all, I would like for you to be sitting in a way that you can be very relaxed and very comfortable. You may wish to lie down. I will give you a few seconds to situate yourself in your chair, on your bed, so that your arms and legs can be relaxed and comfortable, and so that your back can be supported. Now, I would like for you to pick a spot on the wall, comfortably look at it, and as I count downwards from 10, I want you to continue to stare at the spot, until your eyes become very heavy. 10, 9, 8, 7, 6, 5, 4, 3, 2, 1. Now, gently close your eyes, and ignore all the sounds outside of the room. Just concentrate on my voice. Take some very deep breaths, breathing slowly and deeply, letting the air come in and go out. Each time you breathe out, let some of the tension leave your body. Breathe in; breathe out; say to yourself, relax. Let that relaxed feeling spread all over your body. Now, think for a moment about your feet. Let all of the tension flow out of your feet. Let the muscles become very loose and very smooth; very warm. Imagine the blood warming your feet, making them tingly. Think for a moment about your legs, your lower legs, your calves. Let all the tension dissolve out of them, melting away, making them soft and smooth. Your upper legs, your thighs, let them become very warm. Now, at the count of 3 I would like you to be twice as relaxed as you are now. 1, 2, 3. In your mind's eye, concentrate for a moment on your hips, letting them come very loose; muscles in your abdomen— where you may be storing a lot of tension—let that go. Let the blood flow through like the wind through the wheat, carrying good oxygen to all of your body. Continue to breathe regularly and deeply. Think for a second about the many muscles in your back. Mentally tell them to relax, to let go of all tension and stress and anxiety that they may be showing. Imagine the tension knots in your back and in your shoulders dissolving, melting, going away. The muscles in your neck, relax— become very soft—just let them go. All up and down the back of your head and the top of your head, let the tension free, flowing out. Allow the tiny muscles around your eyes to relax, around your jaw. Now, if you are still feeling pain or tension in some part of your body, I'm going to pause for a moment and let you concentrate on that area.

Pause.

Now, while your body is quiet and you are in touch with it, I would like to remind you that the body is like a marvelous machine. It has built-in devices for protecting itself. It has white blood cells that attack and kill the danger cells that enter into it. These danger cells might be cancer cells or some other abnormal cells. Normally, the white blood cells help to protect your body against cancer and other diseases. Remind yourself that within your body, right now, are cells that are very, very powerful. I want you to imagine these, see them becoming active, guarding you, protecting you. See them doing it very, very well. See your white blood cells, any way that makes sense to you, attacking all abnormal cells; attacking the tumor. See them doing their job, like experts, destroying the cancer cells, keeping your body healthy and disease-free. And, now, if you are still receiving some kind of treatment, x-ray or chemotherapy, I want you to see that treatment working effectively inside of your body. I want you to see it operating together with your white blood cells to allow you to return to health; to maintain your health. Remember that when your body is relaxed, like it should be now, your defenses against disease are better, and you are better able to participate with your medical treatment. I would like for you to see yourself being the kind of person that you want to be, doing the things that have meaning for you, achieving and maintaining health. And, I would like for you to congratulate yourself for having spent a few minutes allowing your body to relax and allowing it to function in the best way possible. Now, in a moment I'm going to ask you to draw, in any way that you wish, your thoughts about what you have been imagining and pretending, to see on a journey inside of your body; about your white blood cells, about your treatment, and about your cancer. Now, first, I want you to remember to just relax and to feel good about yourself. I'm going to count to 3, and at the count of 3, I want you to gently open your eyes and begin to listen for the next instructions. 1, 2, 3.

It is fairly obvious that the presentation of the tape has therapeutic implications, even if the patients do not use it on a regular basis. First, some methods of relaxation are offered which presumably produce residual physical benefit, particularly if the patient chooses to adopt them in some fashion at a later time. They may well do so since the benefits of relaxation as an aid to health are spelled out. Second, new information is given to the patient which may be helpful in evoking an attitude change, such as the notion of a surveillance system, a built-in system of defense, and the natural process of healing. Finally, suggestions are provided for cooperation with medical treatment, much of which is quite aversive to the patients and is met with dread and tension which no doubt accentuates side effects.

The tape that is included with the IMAGE-CA has been tested on patients with reading levels as low as second grade, as well as on patients with professional educational attainments. The tape, and indeed the procedure itself, appears to be valid on adult patients with reading levels as low as 4th grade (but not lower). If some mental retardation or brain damage is suspected, we recommend the Ohio Literacy Test. Reported educational levels were not found to correlate with reading levels at the lower end of the spectrum, and hence are not too useful here. Obviously, patients with certain primary or metastatic brain tumors will have difficulty in processing the information required and the validity is questionable. Many such patients appeared to comprehend the taped instructions and benefit from the relaxation exercises nevertheless.

The tape designed for the test is significantly different from the tapes produced by Simonton on virtually every feature except for the overall format of relaxation instructions, together with a discussion for the imaging of the disease, treatment, and immune system. The Simonton tape is designed for regular therapeutic use and patient education and is approximately 18 minutes in length. The relaxation portion on the most recent version lasts 4 minutes, whereas the IMAGE-CA tape relaxation portion lasts 12 minutes and contains more specific suggestions on breathing and on imaging the muscles relaxing.

The Simonton version offers guided imagery suggestions for visualizing the disease, treatment, and immune system components. For example, the suggestion is made to see the cancer as "raw hamburger or liver," "a weak, confused cell," "a blackened area," and the radiation as "millions of bullets of energy," and an explanation is provided for the mode of action of chemotherapy. The IMAGE-CA evaluation tape, on the other hand, attempts to skirt the issue of image programming by not providing specific suggestions.

The Drawings

Patients are requested to draw on 8½ x 11-inch white paper a picture which contains three things: (1) their tumors (or disease, or cancer) as they picture it in their mind's eye; (2) their body's defense against the tumor, or the white blood cells; and (3) their treatment, if any is being received. Frequently, the patients will protest that they cannot draw. It is a good idea to assure these patients that detail, not artistic ability, is what is sought.

A rule of thumb concerning length of time for the drawing is to remember that nothing is to be gained by rushing a patient through the exercise—incomplete drawings waste everyone's time. Again, the patient's situation must be taken into account. Patients who were being given psychotherapy in a week-long residential type setting were allowed to take home several sheets of paper and asked to bring the pictures in the following day. On the other hand, outpatients attending a cancer clinic were requested to complete them during the testing session.

Patients are asked to use reproduction pens or pencils to do the drawings. We are frequently asked why we do not provide colors, since some interesting effects would doubtlessly transpire. We agree. Patients in residence frequently found colors and used them despite the fact that many were living out of suitcases in a motel! There is, in fact, evidence from Bruno Klopfer's work (1957) on the Rorschach that cancer patients have peculiarities in using colors, interestingly enough, and we heartily endorse the extended development of the IMAGE-CA to include this variable. However, it was not consonant with our initial goal of simplifying the complexities of the imagery studies.

The Dialogue

After having completed the drawing, the patient is asked to discuss the three factors that were drawn. Both patient and evaluator should have access to the drawing at this point.

For the bulk of patients, a structured interview format is suggested in order to assure that all the appropriate items will be covered. To this end, a series of questions was developed, and appears on pages 3 and 4 of the IMAGE-CA Interview Record and Scoring Sheet (see Fig. 3). The questions merely form the skeletal basis for the interview procedure. As with any projective instrument, the skill of the administrator is a major determinant of the amount of clinical information that is obtained. (We will discuss the actual scoring procedures and the remainder of the scoring booklet in sections dealing with evaluating the imagery, p. 50.)

Methods for obtaining dialogue may vary for experienced interviewers. The patients who had been involved in a regular relaxation/imagery procedure for several weeks were given 7 minutes to recite the content of their imagery and notes of the dialogue were made by an evaluator. At the termination of the recitation, specific questions were asked in order to gain information on any item on the 14-item scoring sheet that may have been omitted. This procedure was used because the patients were in a group therapy mileu, and the time limit was necessary to allow all patients to have an opportunity for discussion and critique. For patients who are involved in a regular imagery procedure there is virtue in replicating this set of circumstances for data collection, because it allows the patient freedom to go through a recapitulation of the procedure, and valuable information can be offered, based on the more subtle cues of voice inflection and the emotional investment in images.

The patient's responses should be carefully recorded on the Interview Record so that appropriate evaluation may be made after the session. It is quite valuable to tape record

35

the interview session and to transcribe or preserve the tapes so that they form a part of the patient's permanent record, particularly when naive or novice interviewers are used to gather the data.

We have included two examples of skilled interviewing conducted by Donna Kelly-Powell and Harriett Gibbs. The first interview was confined to the questioning procedure and is directed and highly structured. The second was more expansive, primarily because of the investigators' desires to extend the interview to peripheral areas that revealed a great deal about the management of the patient's disease.

Sample Dialogue I: A directed, highly structured approach

Interviewer: Can you describe to me what those cancer cells look like?

Patient: I would imagine they were a massive, moldy thing.

I: Not just the tumor, but the individual cancer cells?

P: Imagine a very irregular shape for the cancer cells.

I: What about size of the irregular shape?

P: Small, about the size of a pinhead.

I: Do they have colors?

P: Dark colors.

I: Do you see them moving around at all?

P: Milling or pulsating is a better word.

I: Where are they moving to?

P: They are just marking time.

I: What are they marking time for?

P: I don't know.

I: How strong do they appear to be?

P: Not very.

I: Kind of weak?

P: That would be a good word.

36

I: Now tell me about your white blood cells, can you see your white blood cells, what do they look like?

P: They are sort of bean-shaped and little on each end and kind of fat in the middle.

I: Why do you think they are shaped that way?

P: Because that's what I was taught in school.

I: Can you see any color to them at all?

P: No.

I: Do you see those moving around?

P: Yes. They travel around all the time.

I: How do they travel?

P: In the bloodstream, to the source of any infection or disease, all the time.

I: Picture again your cancer cells and your white blood cells, both of them, which of them is bigger?

P: The white blood cells are bigger than the cancer cell, not the mass, but the cell.

I: Which do you see more of, the cancer cells or white blood cells?

P: The white blood cells.

I: About how many more do you see?

P: Twice as many.

I: How well do you see those white blood cells as doing their job?

P: Quite well.

I: Are they fighting with the cancer?

P: Engulfing it would be a better word.

I: Do you see them as winning over or losing? How are they doing?

P: Winning.

I: Let's move onto a different picture about the treatment that you receive. What type of treatment did you get?

P: Radiation.

I: Can you picture that? How do you feel that the radiation has worked inside your body to help rid your body of the disease you have?

FIGURE 4. WHITE BLOOD CELLS AND RADIATION ATTACKING
RESIDUAL TUMOR CELLS FROM BREAST MASS (DIALOGUE I)

P: A destruction type of remedy, destroying the cells.

I: How were they destroying it?

P: By radiation.

I: How would you say the radiation was destroying the cancer cells?

P: Doing away with; wiping out; destruction.

I: Do you see the cancer cells as disappearing? How well do you feel that radiation treatment is working to kill the disease?

P: Well, I think it completely got rid of the disease.

I: How many times a day do you think about your cancer and having had cancer?

P: Days go by and I never ever think about it. Very rarely.

I: Would you say maybe once a week?

P: If that often.

I: It may be every two weeks before you even think about it at all?

P: Yes.

I: Open your eyes and look at this picture and describe it to me.

P: The blood cells going after the cancer and the radiation coming down.

I: This is the cancer and this is the white blood cells? (See Figure 4.)

P: Yes.

Sample Dialogue II: An expansive approach

Interviewer: What did your cancer cell look like in your mind's eye when you were relaxed?

Patient: I would say it was sort of a light brown cell with a structure of little nodes inside and the white corpuscle. . . .

I: Wait, let's not leave the cancer cell yet, you said it was brown?

39

P: Light brown with a blister-like appearance.

I: Does it look big or small?

P: It's relatively small.

I: Is it a tough thing?

P: No, it's a membrane and it's not tough at all, in fact, if it wasn't brown you could see through it, be transparent.

I: The stuff inside, what's it made of?

P: It's sort of like the pericardium of the heart, it's like enveloped with a fluid.

I: Can we call that a jelly-like substance?

P: Yes.

I: Does it move around?

P: Oh yes.

I: Can you describe that for me? What does this cell do?

P: Just like a bed of ants, constantly never stopping, but I think a lot of them are consumed by these white corpuscles.

I: When does it move? Where is it going?

P: Just over the body.

I: All over the body?

P: Yes, every place in the muscles, in the tissues. But the good thing about it I guess, is where they can go the white corpuscles can go too.

I: So they don't go somewhere that the treatment or the white cells can't get to it?

P: That's right.

I: When does it move, when is it most active?

P: I'd say it is when you're least active.

I: How does it move, does it have arms?

P: No, there's an involvement there that it moves with, wherever it wants to, just like your blood, it can be a part of your bloodstream. It can get into certain areas, the kidneys, bladder, into the different parts of the body.

I: You know how you beautifully described your cancer cell for me? Let's do the same for the white blood cell now.

P: It's around the same as a cancer cell—in fact the way I depicted a cancer cell was a white corpuscle and something happened to it, I don't know what, it wasn't raised up right, it turned bad and multiplied and they multiply fast. The white corpuscle has the ability to work like a muscle, they can open up and devour the cancer cells, they feed off them then as they kill the cancer cells out in certain sections those white corpuscles are no use to the body anymore and the body has to continue to make new white blood cells. That is why it is of the utmost importance that a cancer patient be instructed on a diet so the body can continue to make these white cells.

I: Describe the white cell for me like you did the cancer cell. What kind of appearance does it have? Does it have a color?

P: It's white in looks and of a jelly-like substance, but it can open up, in other words if there is something that's not right in the body it can defend it.

I: Do you see it as having special arms or any special apparatus to do that?

P: No, just muscle.

I: Just muscle, how does it do it? Does it surround the cell?

P: Yes.

I: Tell me, are there more white blood cells than cancer cells?

P: Well, no there's not. If there were I have a feeling there'd be less cancer. It's according to the patient.

I: What do you think you have?

P: Well, I don't think I have cancer.

I: What does that mean?

P: I think I have been cured.

I: Does that mean you think you have a whole lot of white blood cells?

P: I don't think I have really enough, don't misunderstand me, there's been an illness here and in any illness there's going to be a breakdown of the body as the cancer patient builds these white corpuscles up it seems like there's not enough to envelop all the cancer cells because the cancer cells do multiply fast.

I: Who do you see as winning?

P: I believe I'm going to win.

41

I: So you think even though the white blood cells may be out-numbered they can still take care of the cancer cells?

P: Well, we have to go back to religion and belief. I prayed and it's a matter of soul searching and having the belief that God can do this and I do believe that he has healed me. Now I have aches and pains, but I believe it's due to arthritis, it might fool me, but I'm saying I believe this. I believe that the key is in going about your daily living and helping other people.

I: Getting your mind off yourself and on someone else.

P: That's it, helping other people that's 99% of cancer treatment, I do believe.

I: Let's go back for a bit to a couple of other things about the white blood cell. Are they big in your mind's eye?

P: Yes.

I: Are they bigger than the cancer cell?

P: Yes, about twice as big.

I: Do these white blood cells move around?

P: Yes they do, to an extent but not like cancer cells. In my thought a white corpuscle will devour the cancer cell and it's like they can take so much of eating cancer cells and then they're like elephants, they go over here to a certain spot and collect together because their work is done. They can become like a big sore, sometimes they just burst.

I: In other words once they have done all they can do to fight these cancer cells they collect together and the body gets rid of them?

P: In time, and if the body doesn't get rid of them they can get in the tissues, rot, and that in turn causes a body to sour, the person emits in their breath, in the body, sort of a dead smell. They will collect in the body like a big boil and burst and have to come out, it's in the form of pus, all the cancer cells and corpuscles.

I: When the white cells leave they take the cancer cells with them?

P: Yes, those cancer cells are devoured and I think that's what in my mind would create all the pus and stuff.

42

I: When are these white corpuscles the most active?

P: They're active all the time, but the body just doesn't have enough of them. We've got to be on a strict diet in order for the body to make the cells. Then after they're made, you see, cancer isn't the only thing the white corpuscle has to contend with, they have other diseases they have to handle. It's a pretty good job they have to do.

I: Do you see them as doing a good job?

P: Yes, but it's so hard to get a cancer patient to eat right after treatment. I think you've got to get someone who's been there. I believe if people would be more attentive, encouraging them, showing they're interested in them, that they care, well that's the biggest part of the ball game.

I: You should be able to handle cancer with the proper diet and right thinking?

P: I believe you can delay it even if it is inevitable that cancer is going to take you. I believe your attitude and the right way of thinking can postpone that. I have faith and believe it.

I: Can you describe how you see your treatment working? (Looking at drawing; see Figure 5.) First of all what are the black dots?

P: That was the cancer cell. They were burned to a degree that there's no way that the ones left after surgery are alive. This is the scorched burned area that the radiation caused. This up here is the dead cells.

I: Why are they dead?

P: Because of the treatment.

I: Do you have any picture of what the treatment looks like when it hits the tumor?

P: It's sort of a blast.

I: Is there a color to it? Can you describe it?

P: Yes, there is a color to it, it's so penetrating. I believe it would be so intense; well, a ultraviolet light would be purple, I just believe it's so penetrating that it doesn't have color.

I: So it's just an intense beam or blast of some sort.

P: Yes.

I: And it hits these cells that were over there and what does it do to them?

P: Well, it wastes them to where they don't have the mobility to attack the brain. I believe it's all wasted away during this time. There's also the chance that some of these brown ones can get a free ride in the bloodstream to other parts of the body.

I: These brown ones have been burned?

P: Yes.

I: Have they lost their power?

P: Yes, they've lost their power.

I: How did the treatment kill them?

P: The ray was so intense, you know nothing can live under that, I couldn't if I was to have to.

I: So you saw the treatment as being very powerful?

P: Yes.

I: And effective?

P: Yes, I would say it's effective. I wouldn't want any more of it. I've had quite enough. When a cancer patient goes through this phase of treatment a lot of them like me can't comprehend it's me, me having cancer, having a tumor, just when I thought I had the world by the tail. I said well, old devil like to got me, so I just changed my way of thinking and got my attitude changed, my appearance changed overnight and my whole life changed all the way around and I'm all the better for it.

(Back to drawing for summing up.)

I: This is the cancer cell by itself. This bean-shaped body is the white blood cell.

P: Yes, these are the cancer cells. These (WBC) are just as round as these in appearance but they can open up their muscle and eat the cancer.

I: They're in their open state here encircling this body?

P: Yes.

I: These little brown specks are what's left over after it's eaten.

44

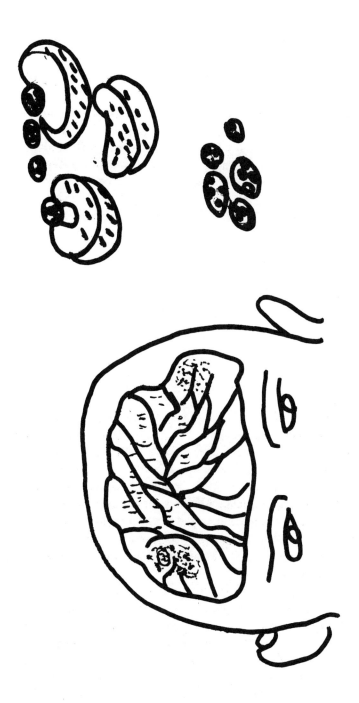

FIGURE 5. WHITE BLOOD CELLS AND METASTATIC BRAIN
CANCER (DIALOGUE II)

P: That's a Walt Disney opinion of it (laughs). It's hard to put it down in words.

I: When you were thinking in your imagination, how clearly did you see this in your mind?

P: I thought of a show I'd seen (movie—Fantastic Voyage). They miniaturized these men and inject them into a vein. That instantly came to my mind—I was going up the bloodstream looking into the area of the intestine and seeing these white corpuscles and how they didn't have any path in mind, but they were moving and they bounced, and each time they could take a cancer cell and devour it and bounce down here and open this side up and do it again.

I: Sounds like it goes pretty fast.

P: Oh, yes.

I: You saw that very clearly?

P: I did.

EVALUATING THE IMAGERY

Scores for the 14 dimensions of the IMAGE-CA are derived from the two types of information previously described: (1) the drawings, and (2) the records of dialogue from structured interview sessions. It is valuable to observe at the onset that frequently there may be no precise statement or figure that corresponds to a particular dimension. However, the high degree of interrater agreement obtained in the norming studies on all factors of the protocol indicates that reliable ratings can be given based on the overall context of the imagery described.

The dimensions were derived from careful study of the imagery described in over 200 patient sessions. They represent points of discussion which patients themselves most frequently used to describe their imagined physical condition. Scoring the IMAGE-CA involves a degree of subjective impression, some familiarity with the disease, and sensitivity to the personality of the cancer patient. Its utility as a predictive device should, therefore, increase as the clinician gains expertise in these areas. Clinically, however, it has immediate value in aiding the researcher or the therapist in focusing on facets of the patient's attitude toward disease that have been shown to correlate either positively or negatively with the course of the malignancy. Ultimately, it offers guidelines for the clinician in aiding the patient to adopt more positive attitudes toward recovery.

The individual dimensions on the IMAGE-CA are discussed in the sections that follow. The rationale for the inclusion of each scale and examples of scoring strategies are also included. The statistical characteristics of the scales will be treated in finer detail in a later section.

The 14 scoring dimensions appear on page 2 of the IMAGE-CA Interview Record and Scoring Sheet (Please refer to Figure 3, p. 30). Judgments based on both drawings and dialogue/interviews are combined to derive the scores. Each factor is rated on a scale of five points, with (1) generally considered weak or ineffective and (5) considered as strong or most desirable. The total IMAGE-CA score is simply the sum of the points obtained on each of the 14 dimensions.

The system for evaluating the imagery or disease has three natural divisions: (1) The Disease (Cancer); (2) The Body's Defenses or Immunity (White Blood Cells); and (3) Treatment (in the case of cancer would usually be radiation, chemotherapy, immunotherapy, surgery, or a combination of these). A fourth division in the analysis of imagery relates to the more subtle cues that are imparted by the patient to the therapist or researcher, and which allow the inclusion of clinical judgment based on less definable, but nevertheless important factors. Each of the items identified below should be considered after carefully reviewing the patient's statement, and with a clear notion of the configuration of the patient's drawings. When the drawings are vague or imprecise, the dialogue may provide the only source of information on which judgments may be formed. On the other hand, with insufficient questioning (or in cases where patients may be either low verbal or aphasic), suppositions are based exclusively on the drawing. However, in most cases we found that when questioning was accomplished according to the format described in the previous section, and when patients were given sufficient time and encouragement to complete the drawings, there was good congruence between them, and virtually all of the information required to complete the scoring sheet could be obtained in one way or another.

After each of the individual disease dimensions has been assigned a scale score of 1—5, a total score is obtained as follows. First, transpose each of the 14 scores to the Summary Data table provided on page 5 of the Interview Record and Scoring Sheet (Figure 3). Next, multiply each of these scores by the weights contained in column (3) of this table to yield weighted scores (in column (4)). By summing these components, one derives a "weighted sum." Finally, a total sten score is derived by locating the weighted sum in the sten conversion tables located on the bottom of page 5 of the scoring booklet. The total sten score can then be entered in the boxes provided on the front page of the scoring booklet for easy reference and comparisons with scores obtained in subsequent administrations. The reader will notice that a "weighted sum" may be derived using either 13 or 14 dimensions. Individuals with relatively little experience using the IMAGE-CA (less than 50 administrations) are advised to omit Dimension 14, the overall clinical evaluation.

In the following section only relevant and composite portions of the drawings are presented, together with an abbreviated dialogue. In all cases the anonymity of the patient has been respected. Here, and in all case history discussions, disease status and other criteria are based on follow-up information obtained approximately 6 months after initial data collection.

DISEASE DIMENSIONS

Dimension 1: Vividness of cancer cells

For this first scale, vividness or clarity of the description is used as the criterion for judgment. Here, the relevant question the researcher should ask is whether from the patient's description a clear image is conveyed of the way the patient sees the tumor. This item was relatively less important than others as a predictor of short-term disease state, but it was retained because of the information it offers on the general ability of the patient to image. In this regard it contributes to the overall validity of the instrument scoring system and serves as a logical initial focus to begin the analysis.

It was frequently observed that patients who were very sick or who suffered recurrent disease in the short-run were able to vividly describe their cancer cells, but were unable to formulate a clear impression of the treatment or immune response. Not surprisingly, a large portion of the drawings of many of the indigent patients was devoted to the cancer cell. Detail was more complete and dialogue was more readily obtained than similar events regarding the white blood cell. It stands to reason that since disease condition is more prominent and more familiar to patients, it would be more vividly described than an immune mechanism which they may know little about and may indeed have little trust in after a diagnosis of malignancy. To reiterate, the vividness of imagery of the cancer cell was not strongly related to disease response and primarily serves to bring the task into focus.

An example of a patient whose imagery was scored "5," or extremely vivid on the disease factor, is presented in Figure 6. Both in terms of the appearance of the cell and the dynamics of interaction, the description comes across extremely clear. This case presents an interesting situation, since based on every indication available including experience as a visual imager, the patient was able to form quite vivid images, yet the description is most definitely not one congruent with a positive attitude toward a return to health.

A low score on this factor is rare, but may come about in any of several ways. Low verbal adult patients (usually those with a reading level of 4th grade or lower) or patients who were unable to comprehend the test because of brain involvement would present a vague description. Generally in these cases the validity of the IMAGE-CA is questionable. A low score on this variable might also occur when a patient erroneously believes that the cancer is no longer there, or refuses to acknowledge the existence of disease. An example

49

FIGURE 6. IMAGERY SCORED HIGH ON VIVIDNESS OF DISEASE
(DIMENSION 1)

The patient relaxes himself three times daily, for
5-15 minutes each time. His relaxation consists of taking
deep breaths, counting backwards, and going over muscle
groups. His liver is described as a small snake, curled
around itself two or three times. Chemotherapy goes to
liver, lung, and neck and is seen as a white spray
hitting the snake. The immune system is a polar bear,
and the bear tears the snake apart. Sometimes, however,
the snake is automatically transformed into a duck or
some other friendly animal. Sometimes it becomes an
airplane. The patient describes feeling actual streams of cold
or hot activity in his body. In describing the immune
system, he says these bears put their paw or tongue
in his clavicle, and work their way through the body
to the lung, liver, and hip. Occasionally, the snake is in
water and this impairs the efficiency of the bears. He
ends his imagery seeing himself healthy and walking on the
beach. He says he feels he has actually done something
with his imagery, but not activated the immune system.
He also said that when he loses emotional control, he feels
he loses physical control in regard to cellular growth.

51

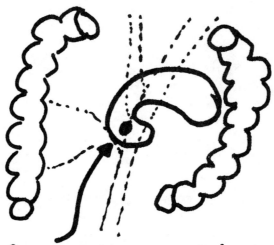

Dehydrated residue
of carcinoma on
the head of the
Pancreas

FIGURE 7. IMAGERY SCORED LOW ON VIVIDNESS OF DISEASE
(DIMENSION 1). PATIENT DENIES EXISTENCE OF CANCER,
DESPITE MEDICAL EVIDENCE TO CONTRARY

*The patient regards chemotherapy as a continuous cleansing
agent. He does not picture himself as having any cancer
currently. Earlier, he saw his tumor as a hard, solid mass with
no protrusions. The radiation affected it rapidly, serving as an
energy source. He said the cancer is now dry and crusted,
but is no longer living. The pancreas, he believed, was
rebuilding. When questioned more about his chemotherapy,
he said he had no real visualization for it, but that it may
simply stir up the white blood cells. He does not envision
any rebuilding process occurring nor any other action between
the white blood cells and cancer cells. He says in his
imagination he cleanses himself with a sprayer, focusing on
any pain. The spray is green soap. He has a vacuum cleaner
that works on his stomach, cleaning out the soap and any
foreign matter. He reiterated that he has no cancer cells
now and that he is angry because he feels he should not be
having a reaction and pain that he now has.*

of this kind of denial is presented in Figure 7. Medical records for this individual indicated active disease, and the patient had been informed accordingly by the physician. Frequently, in using this technique with a patient, there may indeed be no reason to suspect the presence of active cancer (this was true particularly in a group of breast cancer patients included in Normative Group II—many of whom had recent mastectomies). In these cases the patients are asked to recall how the disease appeared prior to surgery. Interestingly, the scores obtained in this manner on the cancer portion were as well distributed as those from patients who were currently being treated for disease.

Dimension 2: Activity of the cancer cells

The second factor relating to the imagery of the cancer cell itself is that of activity. It was selected because of the belief that movement or activity would imply growth or metastasis in the system, and would tap the patient's attitude toward spread of the malignancy. During the sessions there was a high frequency of remarks such as "I can feel the cells crawling down my legs and arms," or "Sometimes when I'm sitting quietly, I can actually feel movement in the tumor area." Since cancer patients are prone to "second-guess" any unusual physical sensation as tumor spread, the factor may be an indirect measure of the anxiety level a patient has regarding recurrent disease. The scale is designed so that the more active or the more *potential* activity the patient attributes to the tumor, the lower the rating. Thus a quiescent description is given a "5" and an exceedingly active depiction receives a "1." Not only is the patient's description of the tumor's activity taken into account (i.e., "it moves sluggish, like a snail," or "fast as lightning"), but also the type of activity that can be imputed to the symbol chosen. Frequently, patients will describe the cancer as animals, which are certainly capable of movement of varying degrees, as compared with descriptions of tumors as blobs or bubbles which have more inert properties.

For example, the drawing in Figure 8 uses the symbology of submarines to represent the cancer cells. This aspect received a low rating, since the ships imply the ability to move. More so, perhaps, they imply a mysteriousness to the movement; an unpredictability; a constant wariness and wondering about the next point of emergency. The crab, a frequently chosen symbol in all groups studied, was also given generally low ratings because of the implications of movement and the unpredictability of the response. Conversely, the use of an animal such as a slug would imply slow or reduced activity, particularly when used in contrast with the active, powerful wolves or dogs representing the white blood cells.

Dimension 3: Strength of cancer cells

The strength of the disease described during the questioning procedure or the potential strength that can be attributed to the image chosen by the patient is used to determine the rating on this scale. This particular factor has been shown to be the most important of the three cancer cell ratings in predicting subsequent disease. The more powerful or immutable the object, the "harder" or tougher the symbol chosen, the less the patient may feel that his cancer is capable of being diminished. Also, it stands to reason that a patient who views the tumor as nondestructible may be less willing to fight to overcome the disease. This scale, which basically represents the patient's attitude toward conquerability of the disease, requires some sensitivity in judgment, since the strength of the image is very much determined by the context of the entire representation.

High scores on this factor are given to potentially fragile or readily destructible images; low scores to images which are strong and hence undesirable from a disease standpoint. Again, the image of the submarine described in Case 2 would be given a low score for several reasons: (1) it is made of metal and constructed to be virtually indestructible; (2) it has power and strength as a vehicle of war; and (3) of prime importance, its comparative strength is excessive. In this case the WBC were described as attacking by shooting pellets, which would not normally affect the structure. In contrast, a high or positive score would be given to cancer symbols which are soft or particularly destructible in the context used.

FIGURE 8. LOW RATING ON ACTIVITY OF CANCER CELLS
(DIMENSION 2)

*The patient says that he spends a lot of time imaging the fluid
in his stomach. He feels that he should be getting to the
source or cause of the fluid rather than just working on it,
per se. He images his chemotherapy going to his abdomen.
He sees his cancer as large masses, all different sizes. The
biggest is about the size of a fist, and all of them look like
black submarines. The white blood cells attack them and
sometimes they score while sometimes they miss and are
annihilated. They look like little pellets going into the cancer.
The cancer is funneled through a canal. When asked what
kills the cancer, the patient said his white blood cells
explode and kill thousands of the cancer cells, but there are
far too many. Chemotherapy was described as a fluid,
greenish in color, which mixes with the fluid in his abdomen.
He says he has no clearer picture of this, and has had no
side effects from his treatment.*

In evaluating the imagery of patients who chose more anatomically valid representations, the same criteria for strength hold. Key phrases such as "they no longer have nuclei" indicate their source of nourishment or integration is removed. Descriptions such as "delicate," or as "collapsing," when exposed to treatment would also indicate low imaged strength.

THE BODY'S DEFENSES

Dimension 4: Vividness of white blood cells

As with Dimension 1 (Vividness of cancer cells), this rating is based on how definite a picture the evaluator can obtain of the patient's imagery of the white blood cells. The ratings on this factor (as with all items involving the white blood cells except Dimension 6) are generally more important in determining short-term outcome of disease than the imagery involving the cancer cell, per se. It is our feeling that the white blood cells usually are symbols on which the patients project much of their own belief system regarding the ability to overcome the disease. A few patients will neglect any description of the white blood cells, regardless of the instructions given to them. Several of our subjects simply fell silent and refused to respond to our requests to discuss this phenomena. Often they became anxious and asked to move on to another topic. It is most important to note these cases. If, indeed, the imagery associated with the white blood cells represents the attitude the patients hold regarding their control over the disease, and if they fail to describe this adequately, it may well mean they feel defenseless or victimized by the disease, with little hope of recovery. Such a patient is described in detail in the section on "The Patients" (p. 97. See also, Figure 16). Despite great elaboration on the drawing, the white blood cells were notably absent.

Frequently, patients respond in a less than credible fashion and draw something which indicates to us clinically that probably no real image, or at best a vague image, of the white blood cells has been formed. On the other hand, many patients invest more energy in describing their immune system than any other component of the imagery. The drawing in Figure 9, for example, leaves little doubt that the patient clearly images the white blood cells in a logically consistent fashion. This patient's description of the drawing reminds one of a dramatization, and her mental picture comes across clearly in her description of both the form and interaction of the white blood cells.

Dimension 5: Activity of white blood cells

This scale focuses on the movement of the white blood cells as described by the patient. Frequently, actual dynamics are not discussed or drawn, and judgments need to be based on the capability of, or inherent movement conveyed in, the image. The white blood cells are often described as moving in waves, or as hordes of soldiers marching, or as simply "floating." The first two cases would be given higher ratings since they are clearly more active representations. Another type of discrimination must also be made when rating this dimensions. Activity which is self-generated (as in the case of motion of people or animals or rapidly moving concrete descriptions of white blood cells) should receive slightly higher ratings than activity which is generated external to the image (as in the case of vacuum cleaners or scrub brushes, which were frequently chosen images). The detail described regarding the activity, and the complexity of the activity (providing it is consistent and makes sense), are also factors which should enter into higher scores. The imagery shown in Figure 9 would obviously be considered desirable on this dimension and would, therefore, receive a high score. Drawings containing snowflakes, bubbles, or other symbols which have no energy source of their own, would be scored low. The Activity dimension, together with that of Strength (Scale 9), seem to be important in evaluating the patient's perception of the effectiveness of the onslaught against disease and the nature of the battle, as it were, to maintain or achieve good health.

FIGURE 9. IMAGERY RATED HIGH ON VIVIDNESS OF WHITE
BLOOD CELLS (DIMENSION 4)

*The patient described her original visualization of cancer
as a large, pointy, solid mass. The chemotherapy was
described as pills exploding like rockets, covering the
cancerous areas and softening and destroying the cancer
cells. She saw the immune system as countless, white-robed
Vikings with shiny helmets. They carried sharp shovels with
hollow handles that contained a healing fluid. The shovels
are used to chop and pick up the destroyed cancer cells and
then toss them into the blood stream to be carried away.
Then the shovels are turned over and they release healing
fluid from the hollow handles. She says the blackness she
images in her chest is going away, and the tumor is left at
a half-moon shape. The center of her chest looks like Swiss
cheese. She mentioned a spontaneous color change of her
tumor which occurred as she was going through a healing
process. She says she has difficulties picturing her tumors
now and that one has shriveled. She now uses her Vikings
to work on her arthritis, releasing soothing fluid.*

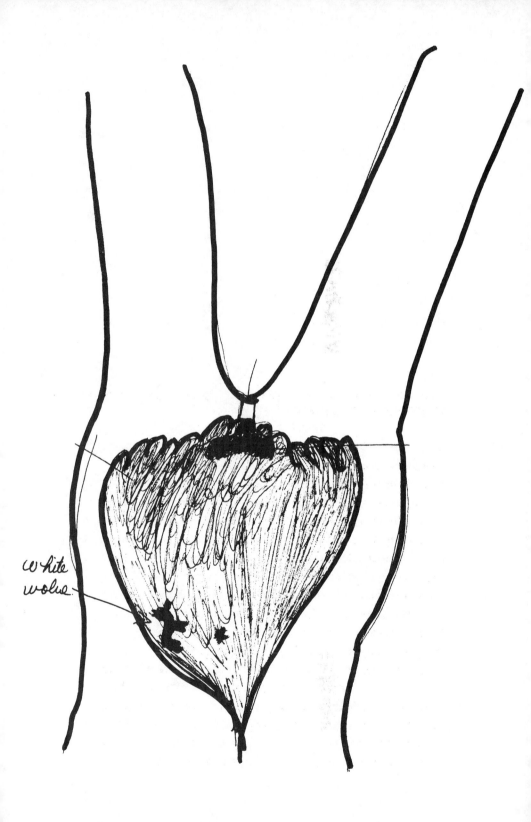

white
wolw.

FIGURE 10. SINGLE, DETAILED WHITE BLOOD CELL

The patient describes her treatment only as some pancreatic
enzymes which look like hordes of tiny green cells covering
her cancer like flies. They gnaw away and fall off when they
are full. She occasionally sees them simultaneously with the
white blood cells. Both her treatment and white blood
cells enter the cancer and eat from the inside out. She has a
new image of a tidal wave of blood containing all of her
body's resources. It has thousands of white wolves
representing her white blood cells. There is an undertow
in the wave and that is important as it pulls back with
suction and attracts the dead sick cells and takes away the
discharge that her cancer is producing. Last week her
cancer was pink red and convoluted like a brain. It is full of
ligmented, confused cells. Now the wolves get chunks and
pieces and it gets smaller. It is confused, and coming
apart from the outside in. The wave is very vigorous and
full of oxygen. She ends her imagery by seeing the
emptiness in her pelvic cavity.

white cells that fight

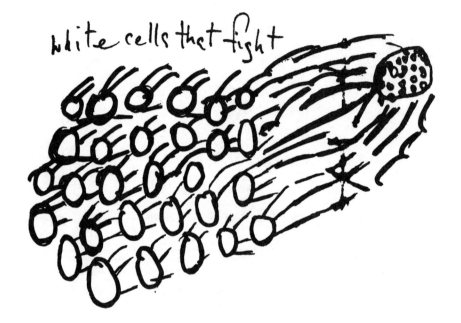

FIGURE 11. SIMPLISTIC DRAWING OF WBC'S, WITH EMPHASIS ON NUMBERS

The patient described her cancer as a small grape. The grape was more fleshy on the inside, and she could frequently see them cutting it [during the mastectomy]. It was difficult for her to describe her cancer cells, but the white blood cells were clear and she described them as big and strong. She could see them going through to the cancer cells and trying to invade them. She could see cancer cells, but only confined to the growth. The growth itself was described as smaller than the white blood cells. The white blood cells are round and much larger and stronger than the cancer cells [4-5 times larger]. She believed that the white blood cells were strong with the help of the physicians and God. In her drawing, the arrows represent the fight that is going on between the white blood cells and the cancer cells.

Dimension 6: Numerosity of white blood cells

This dimension refers to the number of white blood cells relative to the cancer cells. The index is based on both the number drawn and the number described. As with the size factor (Scale 7), questions of the patients must be rather pointed such that some actual numbers are given. Patients without any specified instructions will occasionally draw one detailed white blood cell symbol, yet in their verbal offerings will estimate the number in the hundreds or millions. (See Figure 10.) Other instances have been noted where patients will painstakingly draw many, many white blood cells with no details, but are still able to describe the configuration in some complexity. In both instances, high scores should be given on this factor. Low scores are assigned when no numerical information is presented and when the drawing reveals comparatively few white blood cells. Subsequent validation research has shown that Numerosity, like Scale 1 (Vividness of cancer cell), is not as predictive of disease outcome as some of the other factors, yet it has been retained because of the information it contributes to the overall prediction.

Clinically, the inclusion of this factor is quite valuable. Questioning the patient regarding numbers, and later encouraging the belief that there are, indeed, many of these cells, is conducive to the development of the positive attitudes toward disease outcome which enhance the quality of existence. The scale is one of the more laborious to score, in that it requires the synthesis of a great deal of information. However, interrater reliability was high, which indicates reasonably consistent cues are utilized in the judgment.

It was mentioned above that this score itself does not relate significantly to disease outcome. This is probably an artifact of the open-ended instructions, since it is not specified whether the tumor itself or the individual cells should form the basis for the process. Interestingly, the population of patients who did *not* image on a regular basis (Normative Group II) invested more energy in describing or drawing large numbers of WBC, rather than offering details on the form. For example, the imagery in Figure 11 was given a high rating on this factor, and, as is apparent from inspection of the drawing, the imagery is quite simplistic, with sheer numbers being the only outstanding feature.

Dimension 7: Size of white blood cells

The size of the white blood cell as compared to the size of the cancer cell (i.e., the larger the relative size of the white blood cell the higher the rating given) is a fairly obvious judgment when the imager is highly symbolistic. It is sometimes less obvious when patients use more concrete or factual descriptions of the white blood cell. There may also be some confusion if patients choose to visualize their cancer as a solid tumor, with individual cells having little comparative meaning in this case. Questioning of the patient should focus on the issue of relative size so that the point is made as clearly as possible. The high interrater agreement for this scale indicates again that reading between the lines, so to speak, is effective and reliable.

Size is a viable factor in making judgments about patients' attitude toward sickness and health, possibly because the extent to which any drawing covers a page indicates the amount of energy a patient chooses to invest in a demonstration of this sort. Additionally, the size of the drawing may be related to self-concept, as is the case with human figure drawings. Much of what is thought to be true about self appears to be projected into the image of the white blood cell. On a more fundamental level, the size of the white blood cell relative to the cancer cell merely indicates some intuitive probability about the outcome of the disease.

Representative scoring for the case shown in Figure 12 would be high (4). Here, the patient has drawn a white blood cell several times larger than the cancer cell and described the total tumor area as being about 25 times the diameter of a white blood cell.

Dimension 8: Strength of white blood cells

The estimated strength of the white blood cell is one of the most powerful predictors of short-term disease state. Strength implies destructive capabilities of the symbol and the general effectiveness of the immune system in fighting the

67

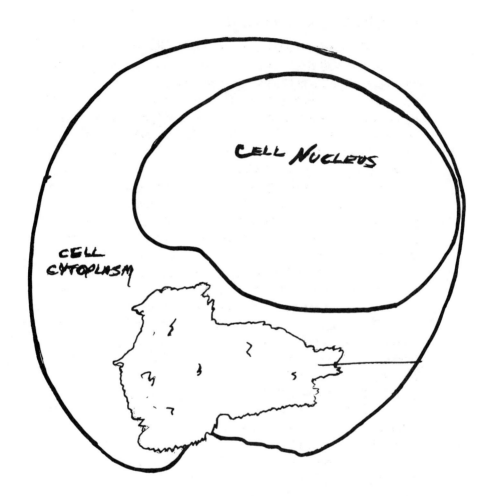

FIGURE 12. IMAGERY SCORED HIGH ON WHITE BLOOD CELL RELATIVE SIZE FACTOR (DIMENSION 7)

The patient meditates for 20 minutes and then begins disease imagery. He acknowledges a creative force within himself and sees this force operating on various parts of his body where there may be some abnormality. He sees it in the thymus, pancreas, adrenal glands, lymph nodes, and nerves. The cancer itself is described as grey matter, while the white blood cells look like they are actually dew and are not seen to him in any symbolic form. He sees the cancer in different parts of the body. At the time of the drawings, it appeared to him as large and located in his liver. The total surface area of the cancer is about 25 times the diameter of the white blood cells. He sees the attack as white blood cells tearing up the cancer and engulfing portions with pseudopods. He said occasionally his cancer feels like concrete and it is necessary in his imagery to bring people into this with hammers and chisels. The white blood cells end with the process of surveillance. He says to him it is not the quantity of cancer that he sees that is important, but the amount of time it takes during his meditation to clear it out.

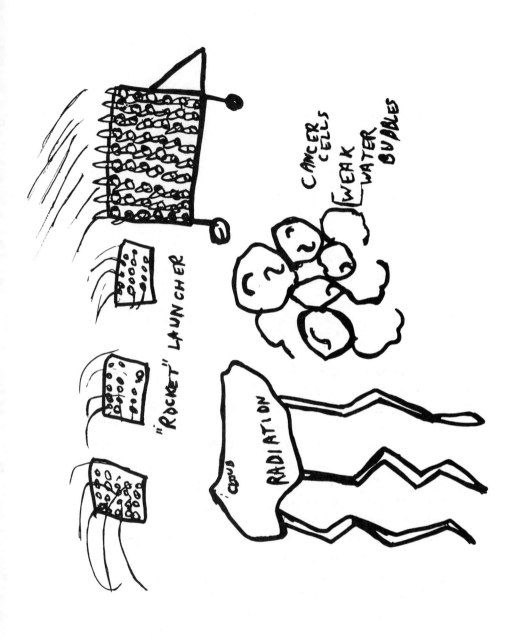

FIGURE 13. POWERFUL IMAGE OF WHITE BLOOD CELL (HIGH SCORE ON DIMENSION 8)

The patient says he sees a violent attack on his cancer, like a blitzkrieg. He has a rocket launcher with 50 cylinders. These represent the white blood cells. He reloads them as the bone marrow regenerates the new cells. All day he sees continuous action. His cancer looks like water bubbles, weak and stupid. There is no space where he used to picture his cancer. They burst as soon as the rockets touch them. He says he sees cancer cells blowing up through normal body processes. His radiation, when he was taking it, was described as an electrical storm, making water into steam, and the sweat eliminated the cancer.

disease. The composite judgment on this dimension includes not only the size and inherent strength in the symbol itself, but most importantly, the nature of the interaction of the white blood cells and the cancer cells. Given a particular description, which body of cells is most likely to win what the majority of patients see as a battle in every sense of the word? The nature of the aggression tells us much about whether the patient's self-image is that of a hapless, passive victim of circumstances, or whether an attempt is being made to psychologically garner resources and defy the cellular proliferation.

Patients view their struggle in a number of qualitatively different and intriguing ways. Frequently, a frenzied attack (tearing, biting, ripping) is described, especially when animals are chosen as symbols. Other patients describe a consistently successful, but more contemplative attack, often with some ritualistic type of movement. The latter cases are usually characterized by deliberation, the former by anger. Both instances would normally be given high ratings, but we assume that the differences are highly representative of other behavior patterns peculiar to the individual patients.

An important cue used to make judgments on this factor is the consistency with which the patient acknowledges the WBC as the winner of the encounter, or as successful in attempts to engulf, dissolve, or otherwise destroy the cancer cell. Many patients express doubt about the totality of the success of the WBC, saying, "Some of the time they win," or "Most of the time they are successful." Generally, when patients see the WBC as losing the fight, especially when they invest some time in describing this event, low scores are given. For example, a "1" or very negative score was given to a patient who described her white blood cells not only as stationary, but also as being attacked and eaten up by the lobster which seemed to symbolize her pain and her cancer cells together. Low ratings should also be given on this dimension when no interaction between the WBC and cancer is described, even though the representations of the cells might be present. Conversely, the "continuous blitzkrieg" action described in Figure 13 was rated high. In this case the cancer cells were weak, stupid water bubbles being attacked by rockets.

THE TREATMENT

Dimension 9: Vividness of treatment

The clarity and conciseness of the treatment being administered is one of the most readily scorable dimensions of the IMAGE-CA. The reason for this, perhaps, is that the description of treatment is usually given with more emotionality, and with the use of more subjectively charged adjectives, than most of the other factors. Patients either seem to regard their treatment as a bane—making them sick rather than well, or are gloriously pleased—attributing it to their disease management. A valuable criteria for judgment is whether or not the description appears well integrated and logical, at least in consistency. When descriptions appear fragmented or when it is hard to follow the train of thought of the patient, low scores should be given. "Treatment," incidentally, is usually defined as surgery, radiation, or chemotherapy. However, many patients choose to discuss nutritional therapy, vitamin therapy, biofeedback, and physical therapy.

There are cases in which cancer patients will not be under medical treatment of any kind, or will not indicate any symbolism for treatment components. The standardization sample had approximately 25% patients with no current medical treatment. Therefore, in order to utilize the formula for weighting and combining all the scales, the evaluator should score persons not on medical treatment as a "3" merely because this figure is the average of all patients and will not add statistical prediction in either direction. However, in order to compare across patients, the scale is necessary for inclusion.

Patients who simply choose not to consider treatment as a viable factor in overcoming disease would be given a "1." Interestingly, it was occasionally omitted altogether from the drawings, despite instructions to the contrary. One of the most vivid descriptions of chemotherapy appears in Figure 14. This patient's output contains an elaborate description of the treatment procedure.

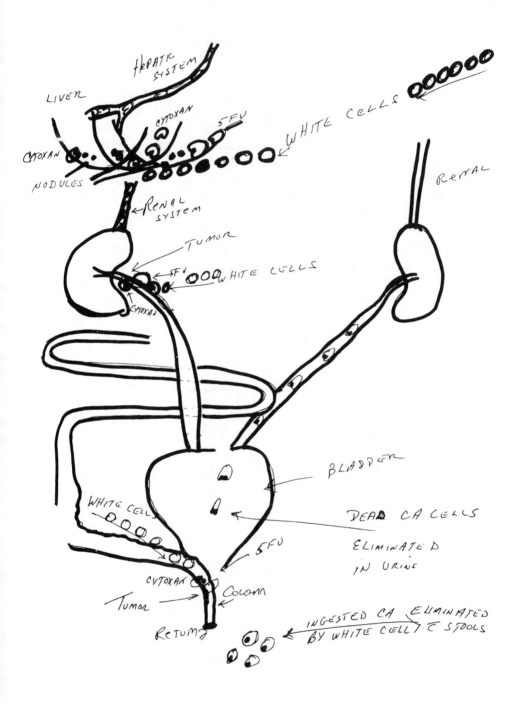

FIGURE 14. VIVID AND COMPLEX DRAWING OF CHEMO-
THERAPY

*The patient describes cancer at each of three sites: [1]
cancer in the liver resembles a black, dot-like nodule;
[2] cancer in the kidney is a velvety braided mass, and
[3] that of the colon is flat and has a smooth finish. It is
black in this instance and always has fewer nodules. He
sees his medication, his cytoxin and 5FU working
synergistically, potentiating one another. The 5FU and
cytoxin have pinchers going into the renal system,
attacking the braided cancer by invasion. Each braid has
one key cell which, when invaded, will allow the whole
thing to let go. It unravels and heals. The white blood cells
are very firm cells with hollow centers that do a cleaning-up
process by ingesting the debris. The chemotherapy generally
is absorbed by the cancer cells or is accepted into the
cancer cells and destroys them from within. He sees
millions of white blood cells.*

75

FIGURE 15. IMAGERY RATED LOW ON EFFECTIVENESS OF TREATMENT (DIMENSION 10)

The patient described in detail two types of white blood cells — waves and breakers which roll over the sand and expose and dig up the sand crabs which are the cancer. The sea gulls [the second type] then grab up the sand crabs. The patient is basically asymptomatic and has been for some time. She imaged the described scene, but could not imagine it being in her body. She always saw the same number of crabs even after the waves had washed over them. She could visualize her immuno-therapy going into her body, but had some revulsion about it and did not see it doing anything.

77

Dimension 10: Effectiveness of treatment

The degree to which the patient images the treatment as capable of combating disease is measured here. On both Scales 9 and 10 there was high interrater reliability on scoring since descriptions are fairly obvious in this respect. Factors such as the amount of space and time allotted to this description enter into the scoring. The identical assumption is also made for this dimension as the previous one. As with the previous scale, if no treatment is indicated simply score this dimension "3."

An example of an imagery rated low in effectiveness is presented in Figure 15. The patient was quite adamant and detailed about the effectiveness of the WBC, yet felt revulsion when describing immunotherapy—unable to see it doing anything.

GENERAL CHARACTERISTICS OF THE IMAGERY

Dimension 11: Symbolism

To score this dimension, a continuum is conceptualized which is anchored at one end by highly symbolic images (a "5"), and by very realistic images at the other end (a "1"). The realistic or concrete images are normally related to the patients' understanding of how the processes would look under a microscope. A common finding is a mixed symbolism, i.e., realistic depictions of cancer cells, but symbolic white blood cells (or vice versa), which would be given a "3." The method of scoring this dimension results in a scale that is not highly correlated to outcome. Yet, the long range findings indicate that one of the most valuable clinical observations is the extent and manner of symbolism of the white blood cells. Symbolism, even a playfulness with the white blood cells, has been repeatedly found in the images of people who do exceptionally well in treatment. It is of some interest that the amount of exposure to biological information does not determine whether symbolic or realistic imagery is chosen.

The type of symbolism selected deserves separate evaluation, since the symbols are recognizable from literature on mythology and archetypes, and many patients envision ancient moralistic battles being fought within their body. Factors that have been found to relate to symbolism are discussed throughout this text, but particularly in the sections on psychodiagnostic correlations and the imagery process and in the case studies.

Dimension 12: Overall strength of imagery

This dimension is dealt with in part in virtually all of the other scales, since it focuses on the patients' overall ability to image. It is a subjective judgment, of course, but is derived from the amount of intensity or emotional investment that a patient seems to give to the percept. As such, the examiner bases considerations on the elaboration of details in the dialogue, the degree to which the person can explain action of the symbols, and the assuredness that a patient imparts that the symbols have actually been experienced and not merely concocted to please the examiner. It is not surprising that this dimension correlates highly with the Betts Questionnaire on Mental Imagery (Betts, 1909)—a measure of perceived vividness of imagery. This factor relates to how *well* a patient seems to be able to image, and not *what* the images consist of. Judgments on the relationship between overall imagery and disease are not included here, but are reserved for Dimension 14.

Dimension 13: Estimated regularity of imagery

As part of the dialogue, the patients are asked to relate how many times a day they participated in the imagery procedure or how frequently they thought about their disease in a positive way. As is the case with all such verbal reports, it requires consideration in view of the socially desirable aspects of the situation. Not having another independent measure of frequency, the patients' statements were given credibility. It should be pointed out that for Normative Group II (medical school patients), denial of disease anxiety, and hence frequency of thought, seem to be the desirable mode, whereas with the patients who were using an imagery form of psychotherapy (Normative Group I), frequency of imagery was desirable. Nevertheless, high scores were related positively to the overall scoring system in both cases.

Dimension 14: Clinical judgment

This scale is the most complex, yet potentially the most powerful of all. It requires an integration of the total reported imagery process, together with a knowledge of psychodynamics and an understanding of the emotional aspects of cancer. Primarily, it requires the sensitivity that comes with experience in working with cancer patients. It is an opportunity for the evaluator to use all the subtle cues imparted by the patient that indicate the patient's ability and willingness to participate in disease management. For naive judges, high variability is to be expected.

This dimension is largely a scale on which the clinician can interject expertise and experience into the protocol. The scoring of the previous dimensions can be done on the basis of objective criteria and little increase in prediction can be gained. However, the clinician should be able to pick up cues, perhaps unconscious ones, to illuminate the richness of a response. For example, the following characteristics have been noted as possible predictors of positive health, but no statistical validation can be formulated since so few cases share commonalities:

(a) Those cases that have a continuity of symbolism appear to be strong in imagery. That is, symbols that can be thought of as being in context with each other and integrated into a single percept are positive signs.

(b) Those symbols that have a high degree of emotional value attached to them are important in prediction. For example, if a person has always been afraid of being overwhelmed by bugs, and uses these ideas in their drawings, their impact has a greater importance than if such characters were spontaneous.

(c) The more the person appears to maintain the symbol as a continuous source of comfort or support, the more favorable the report. For example, the symbol or concept can be utilized as a reference, such as "My watchdogs are usually looking after me," or "My body warriors are at watch *always.*"

SCORING PROCEDURES

In order to determine a patient's overall score, the examiner must combine the ratings of each of the 14 dimensions in three basic steps: (1) transformation of raw ratings (RR) into weighted scores (WS); (2) the summation of the WS (Sum WS); and (3) the transformation of the Sum (WS) to the overall standard score (STEN). The IMAGE-CA scoring sheet provides space for these computations.

The transformation of raw ratings (RR) to weighted scores (WS) is done in order to maximize the relative predictive values for each dimension. There are some dimensions that have greater importance in degree of disease process prediction than others. For example, Dimension 1 (Vividness of cancer cell) has equal importance in prediction as Dimension 2 (perceived activity), and both receive equal weights of unity. However, Dimension 3 (perceived strength of cancer) is empirically more important in the overall scoring and is weighted as being three times the raw rating. The relative weights for each dimension are presented below.

Dimension	1,	2,	3,	4,	5,	6,	7,	8,	9,	10,	11,	12,	13,	14
Weight	1	1	3	3	4	1	3	4	2	3	1	6	1	16

In order to transform the raw ratings to weighted scores, multiply each rating by its respective weight. For example, the WS for a RR of 3 for Dimension 4 would be 9 (i.e., 3 x 3), and a WS for Dimension 14 with an RR of 3 would be 48 (i.e., 16 x 3).

The Sum (WS) is simply the arithmetic sum of the 14 weighted scores (WS). For example, the scores listed below for Patient A yield a Sum (WS) of 102, and the Sum (WS) for Patient B would be 202.

81

	Patient A		Patient B	
Dimension	**RR**	**WS**	**RR**	**WS**
1	3	3	3	3
2	3	3	4	4
3	1	3	4	12
4	1	3	3	9
5	2	8	4	16
6	3	3	4	4
7	4	12	3	9
8	5	20	5	20
9	1	2	4	8
10	1	3	4	12
11	2	2	3	3
12	1	6	3	18
13	2	2	4	4
14	2	32	5	80
Sum (WS)		102		202

In order to depict the meaning of the total scores in relation to an overall distribution, the Sum (WS) is converted into standard scores ranging from 1 to 10 (STENS). The conversion is made by locating in Table 2 below a particular Sum (WS) in the left column and then reading directly across to find the associated STEN score.

For the examiner who does not have a table to consult, or the researcher who wishes to convert to more specific STENS, the formula for conversion is:

$$STEN = \frac{(Sum\ (WS) - 170)}{17} + 5.5 .$$

When only 13 dimensions are evaluated, the sten scale shown in Table 3 should be used. The exact conversion formula in this case is:

$$STEN = \frac{(Sum\ (WS) - 120)}{9.5} + 5.5 .$$

Table 2

CONVERSION OF SUMMED WEIGHTED SCORES
TO STENS USING ALL 14 DIMENSIONS

Sum (WS)	STEN
247 or greater	10
229-246	9
213-228	8
195-212	7
178-194	6
161-177	5
144-160	4
127-143	3
110-126	2
less than 109	1

Table 3

CONVERSION OF SUMMED WEIGHTED SCORES
TO STENS USING 13 DIMENSIONS

Sum (WS)	STEN
165 or greater	10
153-162	9
144-152	8
134-143	7
125-133	6
115-124	5
106-114	4
96-105	3
87-95	2
less than 86	1

Missing or Nonapplicable Ratings

There are times when some dimensions are either inappropriate or missing. For example, there are some patients who are not in treatment, or not taking their medication; therefore, Dimensions 9 (Clarity of treatment) and 10 (Effectiveness of treatment) are unscorable. Also, Dimension 14 (Clinical evaluation) becomes an extremely important criterion as the examiner gains experience. However, while the initial cases may be learning cases, the 14th dimension may be eliminated altogether. The scoring system should, in these instances, be based only upon the first 13 dimensions and their respective weights. Table 3 should be used for sten conversion.

Meaning of the STEN

The intent of any scoring system is to make one record of responses comparable to another. However, it is mandatory that the clinician keep in mind that the usefulness of this instrument may be justified on a broader perspective than "a score." For example, the content and descriptive terminology may be of greater assistance in facilitating communication between doctor and patient, or greater understanding within the patient, than a quantifiable status. Moreover, the dynamic understanding of relating to another person's concerns about their disease is the goal of this technique, and the score is merely a method of condensing the dimensions to one continuum.

With precaution of clinical consideration, the STEN score is descriptive of the sample characteristic from which the technique was normalized, and indicative of predictive prognosis. A person's sten score, presented in STENS, will range from 1 to 10, with respect to a normal distribution with a mean of 5.5 and a standard deviation of 2.0. In terms of variance, this means that patients with scores in the range of 5-6 are in the average range. Scores in the ranges of 3-4 or 7-8 are slightly below or above average. Scores in the 9-10 or 1-2 ranges are considered significantly different from the average response.

1, 2	3, 4	5, 6	7, 8	9, 10
extremely lower	slightly lower	average	slightly higher	extremely higher

In terms of prediction, the meaning of the total STEN is more general and is based on patients' disease process. To facilitate interpretation, the score categories are best divided into three disease processes. Validation research (to be considered in detail later) indicated that patients who received a STEN of 3 or less displayed rapid physical deterioration and died of their cancer in the two-month follow-up. Patients who scored in the 4-7 range had average stability, and those who scored 8 or greater showed remission or significant decrease in tumor size.

To be more precise in score discrimination is not possible at this point in the development of the technique. Perhaps the variances within these categories reflect the degree of judgment on the clinical dimension.

1, 2, 3, 4	5, 6	7, 8, 9, 10
poor prognosis	expected prognosis	excellent prognosis

CHAPTER 3

CASE STUDIES

It is only when dealing with the qualitative portion of the imagery work that we become aware of the extent to which the imagery process is integrated into every facet of the patients' existence: their disease status, their behavioral repertoire, their personality traits. The struggle against death is an awesome battle, for which strategies are developed as a result of lifelong experiences and competencies. In order to demonstrate the relationships between symbols and disease, the richness of the cognitive effort, the extent of the mental involvement in the course of malignancy, portions of case histories are presented. An ever-present task for us is to identify threads of commonality among outstanding patients.

SYMBOLS AS SYMPTOMS

The place or the medium of realization is neither mind nor matter, but that intermediate realm of subtle reality which can be adequately expressed only by the symbol. The symbol is neither abstract nor concrete, neither rational nor irrational, neither real nor unreal, it is always both. . . .

C. G. Jung
Psychology and Alchemy

Just as the body exhibits symptoms which are not the disease itself but unique manifestations of the interaction of the disease with the total body, the psyche does likewise. In the case of the latter, however, symbols become the synthetic representations of the more concrete cognitive processing. The analogy between symbol and symptom can be carried into application, in that the understanding of both symptomatic and symbolic events lead to the diagnosis of a patient's physical functioning and psychological attributes. In essence, we are dealing with the same process. Physically, certain clusters of symptoms have been analyzed over time to the extent that they are rather consistent harbingers of known physical disorders. From a clinical standpoint, the choice of symbolism seems to be likewise appropriate for taxonomy, at least to the extent that various symbols can be related to stabilization or remission, whereas others seem to be associated with physically downhill process.

The use of visualization or imagery in diagnostics is unusual in the scientific sense because, although it is generalized to physical events, the protocol unfolds from a unique level of the personality. The symbolism most commonly relates to a person's framework of what symbols best relate to his or her perceived psychological attributes of the disease process. These symbols are derived from a combination of resources, including memory, dreams, and visions. Many of the symbols identified are ancient archetypal figures; many are traditional representations for figures of good and evil.

The symbols of positive connotation are those representing strength and purity; powerful enough to subdue an enemy—pure enough to do so with justification. Such images frequently take the form of knights or they may appear as Vikings—heroes only slightly removed in time and place from the white knights. The knight is an archaic symbol from fairy tales to which most of us have a common exposure. It is interesting that patients form other associations with the white knight, including the description of their activities which highly resemble a soap commercial from a few years back. Most importantly, patients who use this imagery typically respond favorably in the treatment process.

Other frequently used symbols which appear to be positive predictors of favorable disease process are those of large, powerful animals, especially dogs and bears. These are usually good symbols associated with a healthy attitude.

However, it should be pointed out that it is the competencies that the animal displays in the drama that identify the real meaning of the symbol for the patient. For example, one patient saw bears as his immunological system and snakes representing cancer cells. Sometimes the snakes attacked the bears, and the bears did not have enough strength to fight back, according to his dialogue. So, regardless of the inherent properties of this symbol, the competency was muted. Even though the suggestion is frequently made to patients in a therapeutic situation that they adopt animal imagery, some of them refused, finding it repulsive to see an animal tearing apart a living thing. One patient who had a very weak imagery was instructed to imagine her cancer as raw meat and the white blood cells as polar bears; but she reported it was extremely nauseating to her because of the blood and violence. We feel that a supreme amount of violence, or particularly gory or vicious imagery, may not be particularly advantageous. It may rob the patient of some energy that he or she could invest into the the healing process rather than into the recapitulation of anger and destruction. From a physiological point of view, this frequent recapitulation associated with emotions of anger may be extremely detrimental to the patient's health, especially when there is not an avenue for positively dealing with negative feelings.

Patients with an overall "good" imagery rarely describe mechanical devices, such as vacuum cleaners, automatic sprinklers, shovels, or picks, that might be used to dig out the cancer. A few patients describe only a pair of hands tearing out the cancer or performing some other type of destruction. In no case was this imagery ever associated with a favorable turn in disease. There are many speculations as to whether these symbols characterize a detachment the patient may feel toward his bodily processes or whether they relate to other personality characteristics. Our current feeling is that the symbols are negative in part because they do not have a natural source of energy of their own and hence the patient may feel limited or dependent. Highly destructive elements such as fire, poisons, and acids are not generally described by patients who are doing well. These symbols apparently relate to the degree of discomfort and pain experienced.

In regard to the predictive aspects of imagery, the symbol of ants is a particularly poor sign. It is typically selected by women (never, in fact, has it been used by a male to our knowledge), and it has been used to identify both the white blood cells and cancer cells. Case after case has demonstrated a positive correlation between disease increase and this sign. One psychological interpretation is that ants produce a regenerative trail that is virtually impossible to eradicate. Although one or two ants could be destroyed, it may be impossible to completely defend against this symbol. Crustacean creatures such as crabs, scorpions, lobsters, or even octopi— animals that have in common a tentacle (or a claw) that clings or grabs—are not good symbols from a statistically predictive standpoint. It is not surprising that the word "cancer" is derived from the Latin word for crab, the traditional association being based on a similarity of physical resemblance between the legs of a crab and the growing tumor.

The majority of unhealthy patients tend to be symbolistic in describing the disease element, while the white blood cells are seen as more realistic. The patients with the poorest prognoses spent much more energy symbolizing the cancer cells, perhaps as a way of masking their horror and anxiety associated with the disease. The patients with more favorable prognoses usually reflect more investment of energy in their projections of immunological mechanisms.

Examiners should place emphasis on the content of imagery, since the symbols selected very often are representative of personality traits in the patients. It is important to consider the symbols in context, in the dynamic sense of their projection. One must be cognizant of the existential struggle the patient is attempting to describe. The extent to which the patient can express this enterprise in a meaningful form depends on the person's creativity, background, and personal ability at a given time to convey his feelings in verbal or nonverbal symbols.

THE PATIENTS

Negative Images

A beautiful young woman with breast cancer that had spread to her lungs and clavicle drew the very anatomical pictures shown in Figure 16. She was able to visualize the radiation machine shooting at the cancer cells, the cancer cells trapped in a bulging clavicle, and the chemotherapy in her bloodstream. She was unable to describe or draw anything relating to her white blood cell activity, nor did she picture any interaction taking place between the chemotherapy and the abnormal cells. After 4 days of intensive therapy geared toward attitude change, she was still unable to give a coherent picture of these activities. Her human figure drawing (Figure 17), according to just about anyone's criteria, shows a lack of self-identity. She was, incidentally, trained as an artist. She had experienced two most unsatisfactory relationships with men, very much desired a long-term relationship, but felt she didn't have the energy to begin again. She returned home and died within a few weeks, although according to her physician, "She shouldn't have." Her lesions themselves were minute, and she had been strong and physically active.

A young man with metastatic melanoma was unable to visualize any activity taking place between his white blood cells and his cancer (See Figure 18). The cancer cells appeared as happy clown faces, and the white blood cells as tiny dots. He said that the dots occasionally flirted with the cancer cells, but were never able to attack. During the course of therapy, the patient was able to reduce his Demerol intake by about 75%, but continued to experience new tumor growth.

Animals in Action

Not only is the interaction between cancer cells and white blood cells of some significance, but also the relative strengths and weaknesses of the white blood cells and cancer cells as represented in the imagery. A 14-year-old girl who was diagnosed with cancer of the liver described her white blood cells as large dogs and her cancer cells as slugs (Figure

91

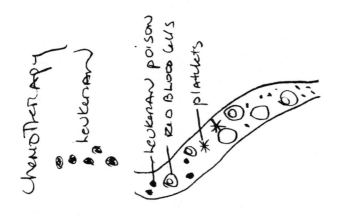

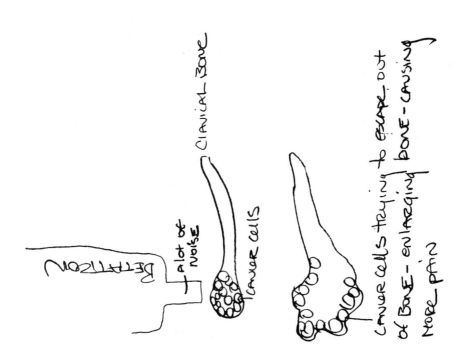

FIGURE 16. ANATOMICAL DRAWING WITH OMISSION
OF WHITE BLOOD CELLS

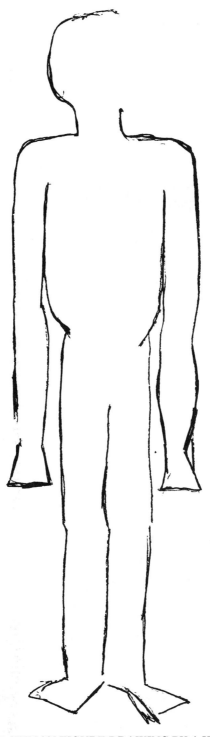

FIGURE 17. HUMAN FIGURE DRAWING BY A YOUNG ARTIST

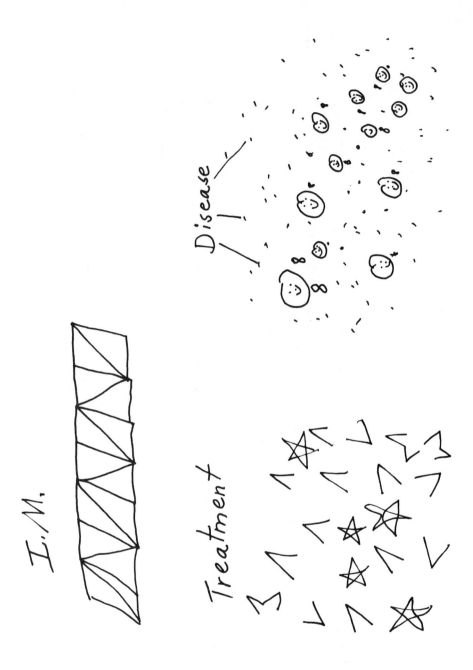

FIGURE 18. CANCER CELLS AS CLOWN FACES

19). She saw her liver as red and perfect except for one dime-sized spot. She described many dogs in her imagery, and they all enjoyed eating the slugs. She has experienced a superb turnaround in her disease, and, according to the last medical report, she is disease-free. It was mentioned previously that many of the patients who do well use large animals to represent their white blood cells, and that while big animals are regarded as "good" imagery, ants or small insects have not been related to good disease management. Figure 20 shows the imagery of a 28-year-old woman with metastatic liver cancer who used the symbol to depict both her cancer and white blood cells. The patient, a lovely, gentle woman and mother of two young children, died within weeks after the drawing was made. Ants—scourge of the homemaker—leave the unending trail which eventually defies the exterminator. This particular patient was virtually identical to several other women in the sample in terms of diagnosis, type of the treatment, previous health history, and age. From our perspective, the single differing characteristic appeared to be in attitude as expressed in the imagery analysis.

Many patients describe their cancer as the traditional crab. As we discussed in the section analyzing content, crabs or crablike creatures are not generally associated with good disease outcome. One breast cancer patient from our indigent population produced the drawing in Figure 21. She visualized her cancer as a red lobster running down her right arm. White blood cells were seen coming from the rest of the body, but were eaten up by the lobster. The lobster was described as moving slowly, with claws coming out.

White Knights

One particular symbol crops up over and over: The white knight as a representation of the immune system. Perhaps it reflects exposure to soap commercials, or maybe to a more basic impression that dates back to the hero on a white horse. This symbol has been observed by other therapists in similar work and in our recent studies with medical school patients. Another beautiful example was drawn by a gifted woman, one of the few who has had minimal disease (cervical

FIGURE 19. WHITE DOGS AND SLUGS

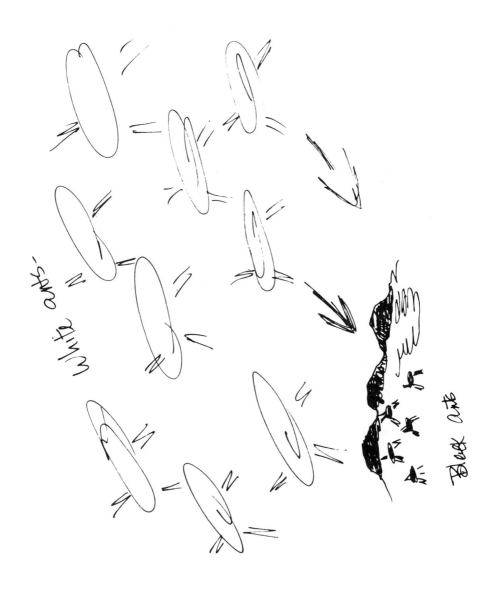

FIGURE 20. WHITE ANTS AND BLACK ANTS

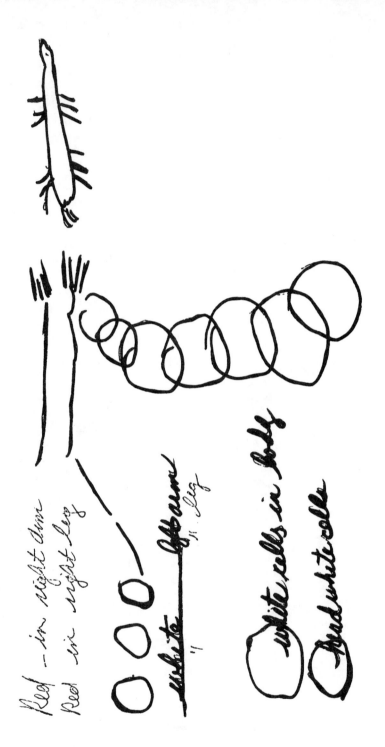

FIGURE 21. CANCER AS A LOBSTER

cancer) and who chose the therapy as a means of preventing recurrence (Figure 22). Support for the consistency of this image across populations was obtained in our interview of a breast cancer patient being treated at the county hospital. She described her white blood cells as armies of knights, attacking the cancer cells with swords. They wore white robes with a cross on the front, "sort of like Sir Richard." Her drawing (Figure 23) is primitive, but her dialogue was virtually identical to the private patients we examined. She had no previous imagery training, per se, and only one exposure to the IMAGE-CA Relaxation and Guided Imagery tape.

The symbol was also used by one of the most unusual patients we have had the opportunity to study. He is a physicist diagnosed over a year before testing with cancer of the pancreas which had spread to other areas. The prognosis for this type of disease is grim, regardless of medical treatment. His imagery deserves a special treatment (See Figure 24). He initially described his cancer cells as armadillos, and his white blood cells as white knights (Figure 25 represents a detailed drawing). The knights had a daily quota (he works for the major organization whose byword is "quota") of creatures they needed to spear on their lancets. They were then wiped off in the bloodstream which contained the chemotherapeutic agent. At one time during his therapy he observed that many of his white knights were dropping or disappearing. He was subsequently informed that his white blood cell count was dropping. Fearing that he would be taken off chemotherapy, he was determined to "peg" the number of white blood cells. After making this decision, the white blood count stabilized, and the chemotherapy continued. Sometime later, he experienced some difficulty in the white knights meeting their daily quota. They were beating the bushes to find the armadillos. Shortly after, he underwent ultrasound diagnosis and there was no evidence of tumor. One of the major problems that he is now confronting in his imagery is a lack of spontaneity. To overcome this, at the conclusion of his meditation he envisions a little boy shaking hands with an adult (Figure 26). During one difficult period recently, he regularly saw the boy on roller skates, gliding by most unobtainably. This very unusual patient seems to be in touch with his

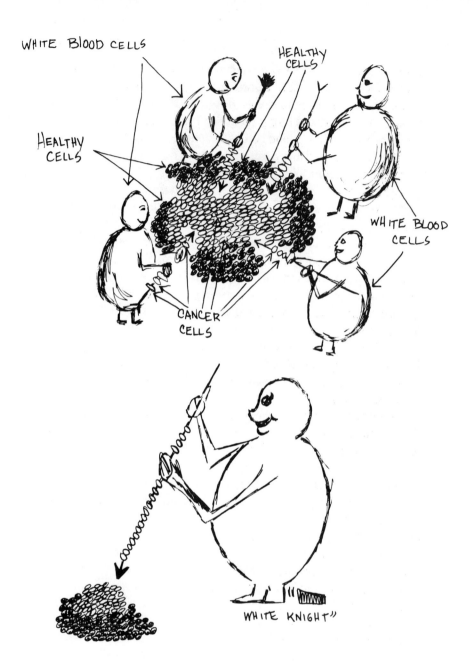

FIGURE 22. WHITE KNIGHTS

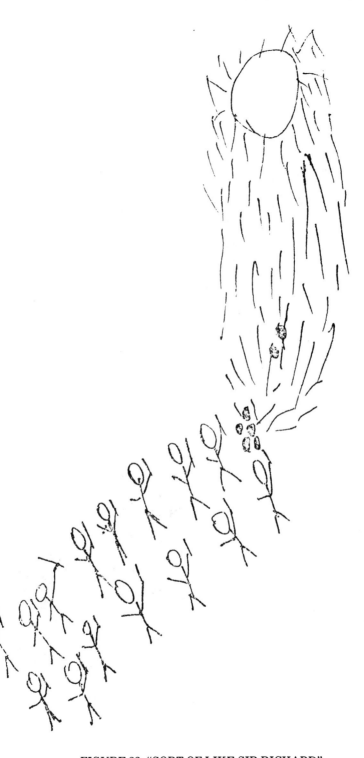

FIGURE 23. "SORT OF LIKE SIR RICHARD"

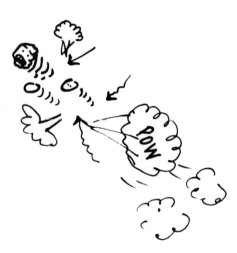

FIGURE 24. WHITE KNIGHTS AND ARMADILLOS

FIGURE 25. DETAILED DRAWING OF WHITE KNIGHT
STABBING ARMADILLO

FIGURE 26. IMAGERY BEYOND DISEASE

emotions, and most in control of the expression of them. Perhaps he is similarly in touch with, and in control of, his physical processes.

Realists vs. Symbolists

The physicist's drawings are highly symbolic in spite of his knowledge of cell activity. The basis of choice of symbolic versus actual representations remains somewhat of a mystery and appears to have only a moderate relationship with disease state and to educational background. Most patients try on both types of images and settle on one that feels right to them—occasionally apologizing for the seemingly fictional nature of their choice. The imagery in Figure 27 was produced by a woman with advanced lympho-sarcoma. She is a clinical psychologist whose disease has been fairly stable over the last year. Her imagery, likewise, has remained unchanged except for an increasing clarity in description and detail in drawings (Figure 28). Much of the imagery of the white blood cell is quite accurate in terms of what is known about phagocytic activity, cellular membrane permeability, and cellular histology.

Treatment Side Effects

The majority of patients examined were receiving either chemotherapy or immunotherapy. The former acts on the principle of any poison or cellular toxin. The cancer cells, which are weak and metabolically confused, are more likely to be destroyed. The healthy tissue is affected to a lesser degree, since the cells' reparative processes are intact. The chemotherapy, therefore, is accompanied by a multitude of side effects produced by its toxic effect on the system. The side effects vary greatly from patient to patient, in some cases being debilitating, and in others, almost indiscernible. They include nausea, vomiting, digestive upsets, hair loss, and blood count changes, to mention a few. The variance can be attributed to the type of chemotherapeutic agent and the general physical condition of the patient. There is also probably a lot of expectancy thrown in for good measure. One

105

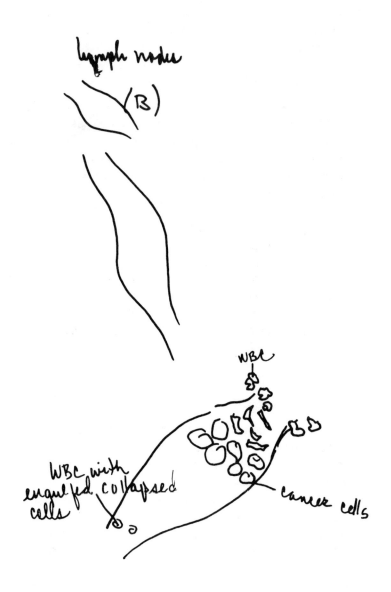

FIGURE 27. ANATOMICAL IMAGERY OF LYMPH NODE

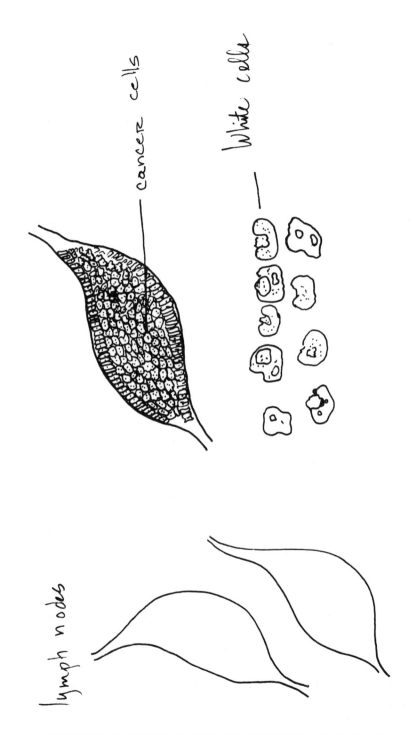

FIGURE 28. DRAWING OF NODES WITH INCREASING CLARITY

patient who was receiving an injection every 2 weeks had pronounced side effects the week following therapy, and then was free from the effects until the day of his next injection, at which time he reported having stomach cramps, nausea, and so forth, prior to administration of the drug. That is difficult to account for by any rebound effect of the drug. The role of expectancy (what a patient "expects" to happen as a result of the treatment) can be studied by examining the patients' descriptions of their images of the chemotherapeutic activity. One of the patients, a woman with primary breast cancer which spread to the liver, remained robust physically and did not even experience the hair loss that usually accompanies her type of treatment. She described her chemotherapy as acting like soy sauce. It was sucked up by the cancer (she used the analogy of the way the liquid is soaked up by a napkin), and the cancer cells were described as shrinking and shriveling. She described it as running off the pink, healthy tissue much like soy sauce runs off bean sprouts (Figure 29).

Sensory Modalities for Imaging

All of the patients seem to use visual imagery, either exclusively or in part. Some seem to be more adept at auditory imagery. In particular, two musicians favored the auditory mode. They would talk through the imagery rather than form mental pictures, which seems a reasonable thing for a musician to do since the favored or trained sensory modality is audition. One of the musicians was diagnosed with an 8 cm lesion in his brain. Prior to radiation, he was aphasic, unable to string two words together. His wife persistently began to involve him in imaging his disease. She talked through the meditation with him, she drew pictures on the back of his hand (using the tactile sense which is notably resistant in the face of even massive brain damage), and found pictures in magazines for him to look at to help in visualization. The initial picture that he drew of his disease was a circle. Within 3 months, he offered us a two-page, beautifully phrased description of his meditation. Within a year he directed a choral group and was free of disease.

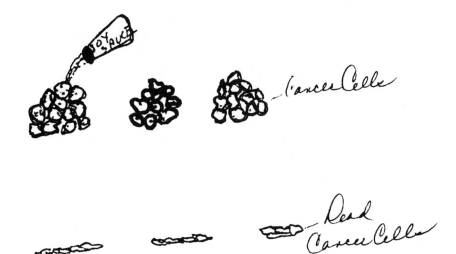

FIGURE 29. CHEMOTHERAPY AS SOY SAUCE

Persistence of Images

Working with a patient to alter imagery so that it reflects a more positive expectancy is frequently readily accomplished. At other times it is a task fraught with trauma and difficulty. In such cases, the reasons underlying the resistance require sensitive investigation. For example, a 73-year-old gentleman with widespread head and neck cancer produced the drawing in Figure 30. The white blood cells are represented by snow flakes falling down on his shoulders. He said he could see no other interaction between the white blood cells and cancer cells, simply that they were "drifting down." Sensing our dissatisfaction with his drawing, he produced a second drawing during his lunch hour which is presented in Figure 31. The differences between the drawings are simply that one has arms and hands and the other does not. Perhaps self-image improved, but certainly the dynamics of his cancer imagery remained unchanged. His tumors continued to grow and he died within a few weeks after presenting the drawings. He remained active until just before his death, continuing to enjoy golf, hunting, and fishing. Pain for him was a rarely experienced phenomena. When questioned about this, he replied that he had devised an imaginary bulldog which would chomp up any painful twinges that he noted. It was suggested many times during the course of a week that he use a symbol similar to the bulldog to represent his white blood cells. He replied, "No, I don't think I could do that. The bulldogs are too powerful." Irrational, perhaps. But on the other hand, dying a painless death at age 73, reflecting upon a good life, and continuing activities which one loves most is a rather enviable position. Any attempts at intervention or convincing the patient to fight to alter the course of the disease may be highly disrespectful of a patient's inner desires.

Surveillance or Monitoring of Imagery

Patients who systematically image their disease process frequently undertake a unique form of surveillance imagery when symptoms abate. The drawing in Figure 32 is an example produced by a woman with metastatic breast

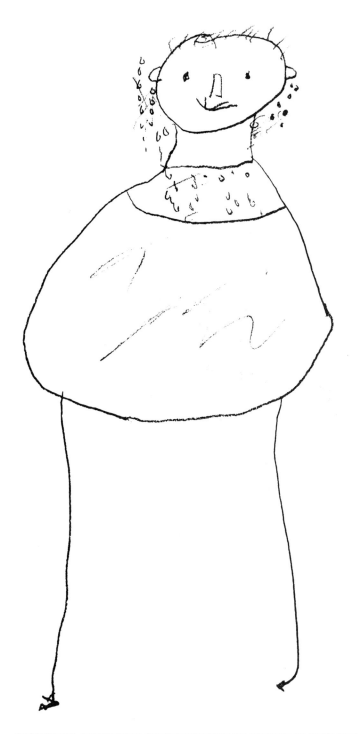

FIGURE 30. EXAMPLE OF INEFFECTIVE WHITE BLOOD CELLS

FIGURE 31. DUPLICATE DRAWING AFTER COACHING

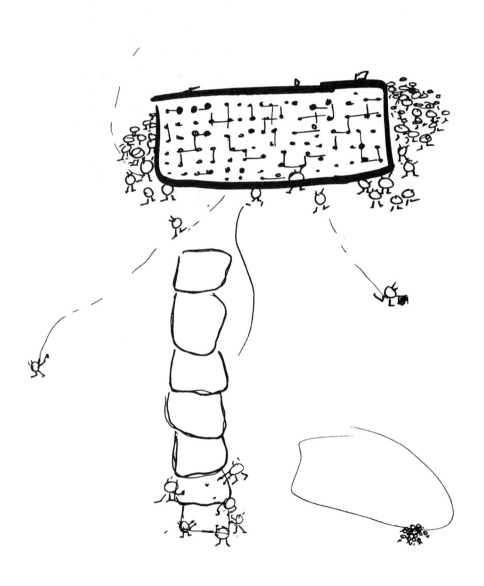

FIGURE 32. CANCER SURVEILLANCE

cancer who, at the time of the drawing, had no evidence of disease according to a bone scan. She had continued an active professional life with only slight interruption during treatment. She envisioned her white blood cells as miniature doctors who, being alerted by a switchboard, travel out into her bloodstream to destroy any abnormal cell that appears. Like many patients, she utilized her disease in a positive way. She gained new and valuable insights into life and it was enriched accordingly. Whatever else the surveillance imagery does, it most certainly gives patients a feeling of involvement in returning to health and, hence, a feeling of being less victimized by any physical setback. It also keeps patients conscious of and in touch with their body's processes.

CHAPTER 4

STANDARDIZATION AND RESEARCH WITH THE TECHNIQUE

The section related to the reliability and validity of the technique is actually a series of researches involved with these issues. In reality, there is no such thing as one validity coefficient for a psychological construct. Rather, the researcher has to correlate the measure with a variety of meaningful constructs in order to articulate the definition of the instrument.

Two normalization studies were conducted on two different samples of the cancer population in order to determine the reliability and validity of the technique. An intercorrelation analysis with other psychological and neurophysiological measures is also presented to clarify the meaning of the imagery dimensions.

NORMATIVE STUDY I

The sample on which a test is standardized should represent as closely as possible the population for which the technique is intended. The distribution of demographic variables with respect to the subjects in the standardization sample is presented in Table 4. The 58 subjects of this study had been diagnosed at the time of admittance as having metastasized cancer and approximately a 5% chance of 5-year survival.

It should be pointed out that the distribution was skewed from the general population on the educational attainment variable with a mean of 17 years. The sample is representative, though, of people who seek psychological services

Table 4

DEMOGRAPHIC DATA OF NORM SAMPLE (N = 58)

Age	Representation	Education	
61-	4%	Below High School	1%
51-60	38%	High School	16%
41-50	29%	Some College	25%
31-40	19%	College Graduate	19%
21-30	6%	Post College	48%
-20	4%		

Sex Types

Males	38%
Females	62%

following diagnosis of a serious disease. Women tend to seek these services more than men, and this sample reflects that trend.

Reliability

The reliability coefficient is designed to describe the degree to which a test is measuring something of substance. In other words, if an instrument was only measuring error variance, there would be no consistency within itself. The reliability of the IMAGE-CA was measured by two methods: (1) interdimensional correlation, and (2) interrater correlation. The intercorrelation matrix of the 14 dimensions is presented in Table 5. The bottom line represents correlations of each dimension with the total score.

If a test is consistent within itself, the dimensions will correlate positively with one another and account for predictive variance in the total score. The correlations presented in Table 5 should be carefully considered by the clinician when analyzing the dimensions separately. The smaller the correlation of a given dimension to the rest of the technique, the less confidence one can have in making inferences concerning the importance of that dimension. For example, Dimension 1, the Vividness of the cancer cells, is less important in the scoring than 12, Overall imagery strength.

Interrater reliability measures the degree to which two or more people perceive the same stimuli independently and rate the dimensions consistently. In this case, two raters scored the protocols without the knowledge of the other's ratings. In fact, one of the raters had absolutely no knowledge of who the patients were or their involvement in the program. The raters had only a record of the interview content and the drawings. The coefficients for each respective dimension are reported in Table 6.

For the observant reader, it should be pointed out that the correlations are all statistically significant, yet have a wide range (.60 - .95). Narrow variances tend to produce lower reliability correlations. This is reflected in the means and standard deviations shown in Table 7.

117

Table 5

INTERCORRELATION MATRIX OF THE 14 DIMENSIONS

	1	2	3	4	5	6	7	8	9	10	11	12	13	14
1	—	.14	−.12	.43	.13	−.17	.13	.18	.23	.24	.22	.30	.06	.09
2		—	.20	.09	.19	.05	.11	.11	.20	.24	−.05	.32	.07	.23
3			—	.09	.32	.34	.19	.42	.25	.26	.06	.51	.17	.42
4				—	.49	.09	.53	.44	.26	.32	.42	.61	.32	.46
5					—	.16	.49	.51	.21	.24	.29	.62	.32	.49
6						—	.11	.12	.03	.09	−.11	.19	.16	.14
7							—	.42	.26	.34	.15	.46	.25	.38
8								—	.13	.13	.17	.61	.20	.46
9									—	.63	−.02	.37	.23	.25
10										—	.16	.49	.28	.48
11											—	.23	−.10	.22
12												—	.35	.79
13													—	.29
14														—
Total Score	.27	.30	.55	.67	.70	.22	.58	.67	.44	.60	.31	.93	.40	.86

Table 6

INTERRATER RELIABILITIES (N = 58)

Scale I	.63	VIII	.79
II	.74	IX	.95
III	.60	X	.87
IV	.82	XI	.87
V	.82	XII	.73
VI	.77	XIII	.84
VII	.73	XIV	.78

Table 7

MEANS AND STANDARD DEVIATIONS OF DIMENSIONS
(N = 58)

Dimension	Mean	Standard Deviation
1	3.82	.84
2	3.47	.71
3	3.40	.90
4	3.88	.82
5	4.00	.79
6	3.64	.83
7	3.66	.71
8	3.67	.90
9	3.34	.85
10	3.24	1.00
11	3.43	1.38
12	3.35	1.00
13	4.05	.89
14	3.00	1.17

The measurements were analyzed as to commensurate levels, not only to compare consistency but also to determine whether the judges were in agreement as to absolute levels. The Agreement Coefficient (Lawlis & Lu, 1972) was computed using as criterion an agreement of judgments within one interval ($K = 1$). The results yielded a significant concordance ($Chi^2 = 607.23$, $p < .0001$), which suggests virtually 100% agreement.

Validity

In consonance with the theory that the only unambiguous way to define constructs is to demonstrate a correlation to external criteria, the combined dimensions were utilized to predict concurrent physiological health status and a 2-month follow-up of health status. In this study health status was based on objective medical criteria: death, evidence of new tumor growth and degenerative disease, stabilized condition, evidence of reduction in existing tumor(s) and positive process, and evidence of complete absence of tumor(s) or disease. Decisions regarding health status were made independent of the scoring of the IMAGE-CA.

Two separate regression analyses were computed. The first analysis utilized 13 dimensions, omitting the clinical judgment scale (Dimension 14). This analysis allowed the researchers to estimate the power of prediction on the basis of primary objective data, similar to the power of prediction of a novice evaluator. Multiple regressions were also computer analyzed utilizing the clinical experience dimension. The validity coefficients for both analyses are presented in Table 8.

The comparison between the two R coefficients for the 2-month follow-up reveals a very important outcome. Even though both predictions were highly significant, the impact of clinical experience is reflected in a 25% better variance coefficient. Therefore, two separate cutoff distributions were derived.

Tables 9 and 10 contain the weights which are assigned to each dimension according to its relative importance to the overall scale. For a novice scorer (one with less

121

Table 8

VALIDITY COEFFICIENTS (Regression)

	R	R adj.
Concurrent Disease Process		
with clinical judgment	.76	.71
Two-month follow-up		
without clinical judgment	.53	.50
with clinical judgment	.78	.76

Table 9

CRITICAL CUTOFF SCORES WITHOUT CLINICAL JUDGMENT
(for novices)

Variable	Weights	Total Score		
1	1			
2	1	Mean = 119.38		
3	3	S.D. = 19.01		
4	3	140 or above =	50%	patients show no
5	4			evidence of disease
6	1	=	70%	show diminished or
7	3			no disease
8	4	=	90%	show stabilized,
9	2			diminished, or no disease
10	3	120 =	54%	show diminished or
11	1			stabilized disease
12	6	=	46%	show new growth or death
13	1	100 or below =	100%	show new disease
				or death

Table 10

CRITICAL CUTOFF SCORES WITH CLINICAL JUDGMENT

Variable	Weights	Total Score
1	1	Mean = 169.26
2	1	S.D. = 34.25
3	3	
4	3	198 or above = 43% of patients show
5	4	no disease
6	1	= 93% of patients show
7	3	regression of tumors
8	4	or no disease
9	2	
10	3	150 or below = 100% of patients show
11	1	new cancer disease
12	6	or died
13	1	
14	16	

than 50 supervised administrations and scorings), the 14th dimension should be omitted and the weights in Table 9 should be used. More experienced clinicians should refer to Table 10.

After multiplying each score by its weight, the resultant products are summed for a total score. If Table 9 is used and the score is 140 or above, the prognosis is excellent for the diminishment of disease. If the score is less than 100, the prognosis is poor. No prediction can be made for scores between 100 and 140. If the clinical opinion can be computed (the highest weight of all the dimensions), much more powerful predictions are possible. Using the weights in Table 10, 93% prediction was obtained for favorable prognosis and 100% for unfavorable (198 - 150). Again, the range between 150 and 198 is uncertain.

Statistical analyses do not reflect the intuition so extremely helpful in determining a patient's investment in his or her own health. The fact that a person's score might be 98 is not a condemnation to an early grave. The health professional is encouraged to use the statistical description to provide a frame of reference for decisions in therapy, but not as the basis for an absolute judgment of health outcome.

NORMATIVE STUDY II [1]

The second validation study for IMAGE-CA substantiated two aspects of the previous results: (1) the reliability of interjudge dimensions, and (2) the concurrent validity of the IMAGE-CA with disease process. However, a more dramatic strategy was to demonstrate that the IMAGE-CA reliability and validity coefficients held up for a sample of cancer patients of a lower socioeconomic level.

The sample of 21 cancer patients treated in a medical school-affiliated county hospital were administered the IMAGE-CA in the standardized form. The demographic data for this sample is presented in Table 11.

[1]The work upon which these data were gathered was performed pursuant to Contract 1-CN-45133 with the National Cancer Institute, Department of Health, Education and Welfare, as part of the patient evaluation effort.

125

Table 11

DEMOGRAPHIC DATA OF THE LOW-SOCIOECONOMIC GROUP

Percentage of Sample	Educational Level
60%	6th-9th grade
25%	4th-6th grade
15%	less than 4th grade (were omitted from analysis)

All subjects were residents of Dallas County with income less than $3,000 annually.

Reliability

Since the purpose of this validation study was to substantiate the findings of the initial work, a broader range of judges was employed. Three judges scored each protocol independently, without the knowledge of other ratings and without any information about the patients. The intercorrelations between the ratings were converted to Fisher Zs, averaged, and converted back to correlation coefficients as averaged reliabilities. These coefficients are presented in Table 12. The ratings were subjected to an agreement analysis using the identical criterion $(K = 1)$ as Study I. The results were significant (Chi^2 = 198.02, p < .0001), indicating 95% agreement.

Validity

The ratings for each dimension were averaged and weighted according to the weights derived in the regression analysis of Study I. In this study, the criteria for concurrent validation were ratings of patient functioning given by the medical school social worker. The particular formula for patient functioning was based on the *Patient Status Form*, a format for listing patient activities. Originally developed by Izsak (1971), the current *Patient Status Form* is an adaptation with more clearly scaled items involving medical and functional rehabilitation areas. A measurement of ability (reliability = .70) is based on the following criteria:

A. General Activity

   Pain
   Nutrition
   Sleep
   Frequency of medical follow-up
   Looking after oneself
   Sexual activity

B. Working Ability

   Attitude toward work
   Work activities

Table 12

AVERAGE RELIABILITIES OF VALIDATION STUDY II

Dimension	1	.84**
	2	.83**
	3	.69**
	4	.67**
	5	.82**
	6	.50*
	7	.60**
	8	.53**
	9	.66**
	10	.63**
	11	.82**
	12	.61**
	13	.59**
	14	.71**

* $p < .025$

** $p < .01$

C. Social Adjustment

Relationship to physician
Relationship to partner
Relationship to children
Relationship to relatives

The *Patient Status Form* is a 14-item questionnaire utilizing a four-level assessment on each of the functional entities, ranging from 3 (no limitation) to 0 (no functionability). The items were summed and divided by the total appropriate for the disease. The resultant overall scores ranged from zero (no function in any area) to 1.00 (fully functional in all entities).

The results of this concurrent validity analysis revealed significant convergence between the IMAGE-CA and the *Patient Status Form* with consideration of Clinical judgment (Dimension 14) held constant ($r = .45$, $p < .025$). Clinical judgment was withheld since, for the most part, the researchers had very little clinical interaction with this particular patient sample. Also, after looking over the protocols, it appeared that the low-socioeconomic-level sample was somewhat different than earlier ones (middle class) with regard to achievement, self-concept, and attraction. When the Clinical judgment was added to the variance of the IMAGE-CA, the validity coefficient remained significant ($r = .37$, $p < .03$) but reduced in predictive variance. In other words, the researchers were correct in assuming negligible ability to predict clinical progress with this group, since the prediction actually added error to the relationship.

A regression analysis was performed to compare the weightings of the 14 dimensions of this study to the weightings in the previous study. The multiple R when adjusted for sample size was .47, very little different from the .44 of the previous weighting system. When the beta weights were compared to the standardization sample, only Dimensions 1 and 14 were relatively different. Dimension 1 (Vividness of cancer cells) had a moderate negative loading instead of a low positive one, and Dimension 14 (Overall clinical judgment) had a moderate positive loading instead of a very high one.

129

Summary

The second validation study did substantiate the first study in major respects. It must be remembered, however, that it was not a replication or cross validation. Neither similar subjects nor similar criterion were utilized. White, middle-class, highly educated cancer patients with Stage IV disease having some background for imagery were administered the technique in the initial formulation. In this second study, low-income, mostly indigent, and racially mixed patients were used. Many of the patients in the latter group were considered primarily postsurgery mastectomy patients whose disease process varied from "no known disease" through widespread metastasis.

Cultural differences were evident in the administration of the instrument. Very little urgency was noted in the second sample, as if their cancer problems were only a small part of their overall lot in life. There were only a few complaints about their future and a tremendous amount of acquiescence. In contrast, the first or higher socioeconomic group seemed to regard the diagnosis as a far greater disaster and were actively seeking out new and promising treatments.

The criterion for the initial group was degree of tumor involvement, whereas, the criterion for the second group was degree of functionality. The choice of criteria was evidently the major concern of each group at this time in their lives. It was noted that the second group did not have a long-term follow-up, an unfortunate consideration since that was the variable that was so predictable in the first study.

The ratings for the studies were made by people trained in psychology and social work with graduate degrees. Specific training in imagery analysis required approximately 50 hours, including administration, scoring, and clinical practice. Competency with the technique probably does not require graduate training per se, but basic interviewing skills and human sensitivities are critical to valid results.

IMAGERY VARIABLES AND PSYCHODIAGNOSTIC RELATIONSHIPS

In order to determine whether the individual dimensions on the IMAGE-CA were related in any way to psychological functioning of the patients, correlations between these items and subscales on a battery of psychodiagnostics were determined (N = 101). The tests used in the study included the Minnesota Multiphasic Personality Inventory (Hathaway & McKinley, 1942), Levenson's Modification of the Locus of Control (Levenson, 1972) which yields three subscales— Internal, Powerful others, and Chance, The Firo-B (Shutz, 1967), and the Profile of Mood States (POMS). Virtually all of the dimensions on the IMAGE-CA related in an understandable fashion to various subscales on the diagnostics. Those variables that were significant are presented in Table 13. The most interesting aspect of the study was the finding that, by and large, the items that involved imaging the cancer were related primarily to scales which could be classified as "Trait" scales, i.e., seem to be reflective of the more permanent and enduring characteristics of the patients. On the other hand, factors related to the imaging of the white blood cells involved a number of mood or "state" characteristics. Thus, these data suggest that white blood cell imaging would be highly variable and highly dependent upon current factors, whereas cancer imaging would be a more constant phenomenon. It should also be pointed out that cancer imaging did not relate to short-term disease progress to the extent that the white blood cell factors did.

In light of these data, perhaps we need to reconsider traditional attempts to understand the premorbid personality characteristics of the cancer patient, and begin to focus more concisely on postdiagnostic psychological response. This is very much in line with our view toward the psychophysiological mechanism involved in the psyche-soma interaction during cancer process. That is, mood directly affects and interacts with immunological enhancement or deficiencies. Attitude toward treatment, as reflected by the imagery Dimensions 9 and 10, seem to be a mixture of state and trait characteristics, as do the last four items involving the more generalized

131

Table 13

IMAGERY VARIABLES AND PSYCHODIAGNOSTIC RELATIONSHIPS
(N = 101)

Imagery Variables	r*	Psychodiagnostic Variables
Cancer		
Dimension 1 - Vividness	.37	Firo B - Wanted inclusion
Dimension 2 - Activity	.20	POMS Confusion
	—.35	Locus of Control Powerful Others
	—.26	Locus of Control Chance
	—.40	Firo B - Wanted Inclusion
Dimension 3 - Strength	—.31	Locus of Control Chance
	—.30	MMPI - scale 1
	—.37	MMPI - scale 7
	—.36	MMPI - scale 8
	—.24	POMS Depression
White Blood Cells		
Dimension 4 - Vividness	—.29	MMPI - scale 5
	.28	Firo B - Wanted Affection
	—.34	MMPI - F scale
	—.26	POMS Tension
	—.24	POMS Depression
	—.29	POMS Anxiety
	—.23	POMS Confusion
Dimension 5 - Activity	—.26	MMPI - F scale
	—.22	POMS Tension
Dimension 6 - Numerosity	—.29	MMPI - scale 4
Dimension 7 - Size	—.23	POMS Anxiety
Dimension 8 - Strength	—.20	POMS Anxiety
	—.34	MMPI - F scale
	—.26	Firo B - Expressed Inclusion
	—.27	POMS Tension
	—.26	POMS Depression
Treatment		
Dimension 9 - Vividness	—.25	POMS Anxiety
Dimension 10 - Effectiveness	—.27	Locus of Control Powerful Others
	—.21	POMS Anxiety
	—.30	MMPI - scale 5
General		
Dimension 11 - Symbolism	—.20	POMS Fatigue
	—.22	POMS Confusion
	—.38	MMPI - Control
	.54	Firo B - Wanted Affection
	—.31	POMS Depression
	—.37	POMS Anxiety
Dimension 12 - Overall Strength of Imagery	—.33	MMPI - scale 5
	—.28	MMPI - scale 8
	—.34	Locus of Control Chance
	—.26	MMPI - scale 2
	—.24	POMS Depression
	—.27	POMS Anxiety
Dimension 13 - Regularity of Imaging	—.29	MMPI - F scale
	—.27	MMPI - scale 7
	.31	Locus of Control Internal
	—.27	POMS Tension
	—.26	POMS Depression
	—.29	POMS Confusion
Dimension 14 - Imagery and Disease Management	—.26	MMPI - scale 1
	—.30	Firo B - Expressed Inclusion
	.30	Firo B - Wanted Control

*$p < .05$

gestalt of the imagery process. A more complete discussion and interpretation of the dimensions follows.

CORRELATIONS OF THE INDIVIDUAL DIMENSIONS WITH PSYCHODIAGNOSTIC VARIABLES

Dimension 1: Vividness of cancer cells

The solitary item correlated with Vividness of cancer cells was the Firo-B scale, Wanted Inclusion. It appears that this scale basically reflects the psychological characteristic of needing to be part of social groups, perhaps requiring social approval, and, indeed, some fear of solitude. This scale is generally perplexing because, even though it seems vital to the imaging process itself, it does not correlate with rehabilitation variables, disease variables, nor apparently with psychological characteristics.

Dimension 2: Activity of cancer cells

The patients who saw their tumors as less active (and hence received higher scores) were more confused, gave moderate or little attribution to external control factors, and expressed a tendency to be very self-sufficient. The overall psychological description seems to impart some degree of internal strength. If this belief is of long standing, then a mood of prevailing confusion is quite understandable. Cellular proliferation or cells out of control are not consistent with the psychological dimensions in this category.

Dimension 3: Strength of cancer cells

The weaker a patient imaged the cancer cells (and hence the higher score), the less belief that chance was a factor of control. Basically, however, the scale seems to reflect both depression and anxiety: the less anxious, less depressed patients apparently envision the cancer cells as weaker, while the more depressed and anxious patients describe their cancer cells as relatively more overbearing.

Dimension 4: Vividness of white blood cells

As mentioned above, in this analysis the white blood cell dimensions related primarily to the mood state scales. Among the significant correlations, tension, depression, anxiety, and confusion were all determined by the Profile of Mood States. This seems to indicate that the more vivid a patient's imagery, the less expression of the basic negative state. Additionally, the patients who score high on this dimension typically seem to be quite honest and express vocational and avocational interests which are typical for their sex.

Dimension 5: Activity of white blood cells

Patients who describe their white blood cells as being quite active seem to be rather open, honest, and relatively less tense. This dimension seems to reflect little in the way of psychological characteristics, yet was found to be highly predictive of current follow-up disease and rehabilitation status.

Dimension 6: Numerosity of white blood cells.

The single scale on the psychodiagnostic battery which correlated significantly with the number of white blood cells described by the patient was MMPI Scale 4 which in a normal population probably describes conformity vs. nonconformity. The more white blood cells relative to cancer cells the patient described, the more conforming according to the MMPI scale. Thus, a social desirability factor in reporting numbers may be operative in this case.

Dimension 7: Size of white blood cells.

The relative size of the white blood cell described by the patient appeared in this study to be related only to state anxiety. The less anxious the patient, the larger the relative size of the white blood cell described.

Dimension 8: Strength of white blood cells

As with Dimension 7, low state anxiety seemed to be related to the positive attribution of strength to the white

134

blood cell. Other state characteristics, such as low tension and lack of depression, were similarly related. Patients who respond in a fashion indicative of self-sufficiency also identified more strength in their white blood cells. The MMPI F scale, a validity index, is also predictive of this dimension. Based on an interpretation of this scale, one can conclude that patients who comprehend the task, are cooperative, and who do not seem to be disorganized by severe anxiety states generally score high on white blood cell variables.

Dimension 9: Vividness of treatment

The clearer and more comprehensively a patient is able to relate the *modus operandi* of the treatment, the less state anxiety exhibited on the psychodiagnostic instruments. This was the only factor found to statistically relate to this dimension. Again, we point out that highly anxious patients obtain low scores on many of the dimensions of the IMAGE-CA. Effective imagery seems to have all the characteristics of a successful desensitization process.

Dimension 10: Effectiveness of treatment

Patients who described their treatment in a way that appears to be more effective generally had less expressed belief in the external control of powerful other people as manipulators in their lives and were more likely to exhibit interests typical of the same sex. Anxiety, again, was negatively correlated with this dimension of strength of treatment.

Dimension 11: Symbolism of treatment

The more symbolistic the patient's imaging process, the less momentary fatigue and confusion, depression, and anxiety he exhibited. Patients high on this dimension also expressed needing more affection and attention, and could possibly be identified as somewhat lacking in self-control. To be quite colloquial, patients who feel "good," and yet seem to require some type of nurturance typically use more symbolistic imagery. The process appears to be related to

135

these factors and totally unrelated to either rehabilitation or disease status.

Dimension 12: Overall strength of imagery

Patients who score high on this item, reflecting how well the evaluator thinks the patient is able to image, are less depressed and anxious, more coherent and less confused, and more sex-typed than patients who appear to be weak imagers. Chance also seems to be given little emphasis as a ruling ingredient in the determination of their lives.

Dimension 13: Regularity of imagery

Based on these results, patients who participate in a highly regular process of guided imagery are also less tense, less depressed, and less confused. They are also internally controlled individuals who exhibit some orderliness, or perhaps even rigidity and meticulousness.

Dimension 14: Relationship to disease management

Patients who were judged to have subsequent good disease management based on their overall imagery are typically less depressed, require less social interaction with other people, and are more passive in the sense of acknowledging a willingness to advocate control or management of various factors in their lives. While this appears somewhat anomalous, it makes sense when one considers that the patients who score high on this item may be expressing a willingness or desire to have their disease controlled.

NEUROPHYSIOLOGICAL CORRELATES OF IMAGERY

Few individuals lack the ability to evoke images. However, there is considerable variance in the degree of clarity and vividness of images, and presumably concomitant differences in neurological functioning during the process. Therefore, it seemed to be important to relate imagery to the autonomic experiences of the individual in some fashion. The original research, conducted by Ms. Donna Kelly-Powell, investigated imagery from a selected group of cancer patients for whom visualization or the imagery process was a significant part of the method of treatment they were receiving for their disease and whose data were included in Normative Group I. The first phase of her study was primarily concerned with a comparison of various imagery measures, including EEG recordings, between experienced and inexperienced imagers. In Phase 2 of the study, the EEG measures were compared with the scores on the IMAGE-CA. In addition, ratings on the IMAGE-CA were correlated with pulse rate, a measure of physiological anxiety, and the Betts Questionnaire on Mental Imagery (Betts, 1909).

The results in Phase 1 confirmed the notions suggested by Brown (1974) and others that visual imagery is accompanied by alpha suppression in inexperienced imagers, whereas experienced imagers are able to sustain alpha during imagery. No significant differences were noted on the Betts between experienced and inexperienced groups. The Betts measures an individual's perception of his own ability to image vividly. Since no differences were noted in perceived ability between these two groups of patients, we must seriously question utility of the instrument—since imagery, like most functions, is likely to increase with practice. Self-report on vividness of imagery is probably highly contaminated by the obvious social desirability of certain answers and the subtle and not-so-subtle pressures that patients must feel in a psychotherapeutic milieu that focuses on an imagery procedure. Alpha suppression, then, rather than the Betts, appears to be the most valuable predictor of imagery experience.

The IMAGE-CA dimensions correlated primarily with the stage of imagery during which patients were asked to imagine the process of the cancer cells being attacked. Both Symbolism (Dimension 11) and Overall clinical judgment (Dimension 14) appear to be the primary covariants with the alpha measure. Decreases in alpha during this imaging period appear to be correlated with both increased symbolism and linked with the clinical judgment regarding prognosis. In this particular study, Dimension 12, which is primarily an estimation of patients' ability to image, and the overall prognosis used to determine the judgment on the 14th dimension seemed to be related to the Betts Questionnaire. The pulse rate measures also showed trends toward significant correlations with the symbolism score.

Research using more subjects, multiple electrode placements, and more sophisticated controls is needed in order for the relationship between alpha levels and vividness of imagery to be fully understood. The significance of the increased or sustained alpha levels noted in the experienced imagers should also be studies further in other applications.

ADDITIONAL VALIDATION STUDIES

Robert Trestman (1981) conducted an exhaustive replication and extension of the data base used to construct the Image-CA. He administered the Image-CA to 48 adult cancer patients, collected medical histories, blood chemistry and hematological variables, and administered a psychological battery that included the California Psychological Inventory (CPI), the Imaginal Processes Inventory (IPI), the Draw-a-Person Test (DAP), and a Necker cube rotation task. All instruments and the battery were factor analyzed, and the factor structure of the psychological tests was compared on a group of healthy college students.

The results of this study are highly complex, and any brief summary can only highlight portions of the undertaking. Here, we'll make those points most relevant to the Image-CA. The patient sample represented a more moderate group than the Image-CA normative samples, both in terms of socioeconomic status and seriousness of disease. Only 19 had Stage IV cancer, and none were apparently involved in formal groups which used imagery in a health-related manner. Any comparisons with the Image-CA normative samples should be made with these differences in mind. In particular, the weighted summed score obtained on his subjects was not found to be predictive of current or follow-up disease status, which might be expected given a sample that had very few subjects in the extreme category of remission of Stage IV cancer, and none who had died.

First of all, in his study Trestman found the interrater reliability of the Image-CA scoring procedure to be .86 ($p <$ .01). Based on the data obtained from his sample, Trestman analyzed the factor structure of the Image-CA, derived by the principal factor solution of factor analysis, after varimax rotation (Table 14). Four factors were identified. Factor I included primarily the vividness dimensions; symbolism related exclusively to Factor II; Factor III was considered a white blood cell factor based upon its significant loadings; and Factor IV was described as a cancer factor. In view of the interpretable factor structure, Trestman suggested that the Image-CA is not unidimensional and that a pattern of subscores might be more meaningful than a single weighted sum as suggested in the original version.

Table 14

FACTOR STRUCTURE FOR THE IMAGE-CA

(Interpreted Variable-Factor Correlations [$r > 0.40$] are underlined.)

Variable	Factor			
	I	II	III	IV
1 Cancer Vividness	0.60	0.19	0.08	−0.02
2 Cancer Activity	0.13	−0.22	0.00	0.83
3 Cancer Strength	−0.07	0.14	0.19	0.64
4 WBC Vividness	0.44	0.51	0.11	0.03
5 WBC Activity	0.22	0.37	0.43	−0.17
6 WBC Number	0.27	0.10	0.48	0.24
7 WBC Size	0.15	0.31	0.24	0.24
8 WBC Strength	0.03	0.17	0.94	0.20
9 Treatment Vividness	0.48	0.15	0.07	0.00
10 Treatment Effect	0.44	0.09	0.20	0.12
11 Imagery Symbolism	0.24	0.87	0.22	−0.02
12 Imagery Strength	0.69	0.59	0.15	−0.01
13 Imagery Regularity	0.47	−0.27	−0.18	−0.37
14 Clinical Impression	0.66	0.42	0.47	0.08

Trestman further observed that the factor structure of the Image-CA was unique in combination with other measures. It loaded only on its own factor and no other, and consequently it contributed a significant amount of variance. Generally, it was found to be independent of the numerous other instruments he administered. The Image-CA was the instrument most significantly correlated to medical variables (both hematology and blood chemistry) in a broad, complex pattern of relationships. He concludes, "The Image-CA taps a dimension separate from those measured by the remaining tests. It would, therefore, seem that one's assumptions and expectations about cancer are neither a simple product of one's style of, and ability to, manage stress nor of one's pattern of imagery use" (Trestman, 1981, p. 163).

Trestman added additional dimensions to the original scoring system, and these significantly increased the ability of the imagery of the cancer cells, per se, to predict medical history and blood measures. (In its current formulation, the cancer cells are the relatively weaker predictors, as compared to the white blood cells and the more general Dimensions 11-14.) Trestman's dimensions, which included color, dangerousness, strength, and activity, were based on the metaphorical content gleaned from the verbal description of the cancer cells. In other words, these dimensions were based upon the *figurative* attributes of the *reported* cancer images, rather than upon how the person described the drawing. Four specific color categories were derived: black/red, light colors (pink, grey, white, or yellow), dark colors (such as dark grey), and no color or clear. Interestingly, 13 of 14 people whose disease status was described as "good" described their cancer as red or black, while 8 of 11 with poor status described their cancers in lighter colors. Dangerousness, strength, and activity were scored on a scale of 1 to 5, with 5 representing more of the quality, and 1 representing less. These categories may be tapped in conjunction with the original Image-CA questions on cancer, and the metaphorical quality of the imagery would be expected to influence the rater's judgment, whether or not they were directed to use it as a consideration. Nevertheless, it is clearly an important focus, particularly since the metaphoric dimensions increase the ability of the

140

instrument to predict medical variables in this sample. Table 15 contains a correlation matrix of selected Image-CA dimensions (cancer activity and strength and white blood cell activity and strength) and the metaphorical dimensions, together with demographic and medical variables, and the other psychological scales administered.

Predictive Studies

Whether the images of cancer, as measured by the Image-CA, are correlative factors reflecting a sort of "body wisdom," or whether they could also be causative in terms of inducing physical change, has remained at the core of the controversy surrounding the use of imagery as a therapeutic tool. The fact that the Image-CA was predictive of subsequent disease change as well as the literature reviewed earlier which demonstrated the potency of imagery in altering physiological function would suggest an element of causality. In order for imagery to have any effect on cancer remission, though, it would logically have to impact upon and, in some unknown way, direct the functioning of the immune system. A series of investigations designed to test this notion was conducted by John Schneider, C. Wayne Smith, and Sarah Whitcher (1983) and Christine Minning at Michigan State University (1981). The studies are of great interest here because of the demonstration of control over specific immune functions, and also because of the modification of the Image-CA that was used to correlate blood variables with imagery.

These researches tested the ability of healthy subjects to alter the behavior of one type of white blood cell—the neutrophil. Neutrophils were chosen because they constitute a high percentage of the white blood cell population and play a significant role in response to bacterial infections and in the inflammatory response. They are also known to be highly sensitive to emotional stress.

Three dependent measures were chosen as being indicative of immune response: (1) White blood count (WBC).

141

Table 15

SIGNIFICANT CORRELATIONS OF IMAGE-CA WITH OTHER MEASURES

| | IMAGE-CA | | | | | Metaphoric Imagery | | |
| | Cancer | | WBC | | | | Cancer | |
Variable	AC	ST	AC	ST	CO	DA	ST	AC
A. **CPI:**								
1 Objectivity		.27	.27	.26			−.30	
2 Intellect.					−.38			
3 Logical An.			.27	.27			−.26	
4 Concentra.							−.32	
5 Tol. Ambig.			.30		−.39			
6 Regr. Ego					−.35			
7 Sublimation		.28						
8 Substitute			.31	.28			−.33	
9 Suppression		.26	.25	.39*	−.35		−.49*	
10 Summed Cope			.26					
B. **DAP-Anxiety:**								
1 Reinforce						.28		
2 Placement			−.29	−.31			.32	
3 Omission			−.26	−.27			.29	
4 Size	−.34							
5 Head Size	−.33						.39*	
6 Transparent		−.29					.37*	
7 Line Absent	−.30					.28	.41*	
8 Ver. Imbal.	−.26	−.27		−.26			.37*	
9 Empha. Line		−.31		−.26			.31	
10 Distortion							.32	
11 Head Simpl.							.38*	
12 Body Simpl.							.27	
C. **IPI:**								
1 Positive		−.31			−.48*			
2 Guilt			.29					
D. **IMAGE-CA:**								
1 CA Vivid	.50*	.50*				.38*		.41*
2 CA Active					−.44	−.30	−.50*	−.42*
3 CA Strong				.34	.38	−.60*	−.82*	−.52*
4 WBC Vivid			.31	.34				
5 WBC Active				.43*				
6 WBC Number	.26		.36*	.51*				

	12	15	25	27	24	11	24	13
7 WBC Size								.33
8 WBC Strong			.43*		−.36		−.33	.34
9 Symbolism			.52*	.38*	−.53*			.27
10 Strength		.34	.48*	.36*		.33	.33	
11 Regularity	.31	−.32		−.27	−.43		−.33	
12 Total 1-13		.39*	.52*	.60*				
13 Clin. Impr.			.47*	.56*				
14 Total 1-14	.26	.37*	.52*	.61*	−.34		−.30	.26
E. Age								
F. Sex								
G. SES		−.25						
H. Religion:								
1 Freq. Atten.		−.26	.30		−.41			
2 Importance	.25		.32	.27		−.32		
I. Medical His.:								
1 Time Diag.			.32		.45			
2 Stage Now					.34			
3 Occurrence					.61*			
4 Status					.38			
5 Num. Treat.					.50*			
6 Complica.					.34			
7 Now Treat.								
8 Performance					−.46*			
9 Wt. Stable				.27	−.40		−.32	.25
10 Wt. Change				.34	−.50*			
11 Surgeries				.50*	−.48*			
12 Chemother.								
13 Radiation	−.26		−.27		.63*			−.33
J. Blood Meas.:								
1 RBC			.29	.32		.33		.30
2 HGB			.30	.27		.35*		.31
3 HCT						.36*	.25	.42*
4 Platelet		−.30	.28			.29		
5 WBC								.25
6 Protein						.26		
7 Phosphorus			−.25	−.32				
8 Uric Acid			.29					
9 Creatinine	.37*			.25				
10 Alk. Phos.	.26							
11 SGOT					.35			
Total	**12**	**15**	**25**	**27**	**24**	**11**	**24**	**13**

*p < 0.01; All others significant at p < 0.05.

This reflects the absolute numbers of white blood cells in the blood stream. A decrease in WBC in a *short* period of time indicates the extent to which they have left the blood stream or attached to the vessel walls. An increase in WBC in a short period could be the result of either a state of decreased readiness to carry out immune function, increased output of cells from the bone marrow, or increased activity on the part of the individual, such as aerobic exercise.

(2) Adherence (Ad). The adherence ability of the cell indicates its readiness for motility and migration from the vessel to the site of inflammation. The neutrophils, normally free floating in the blood stream, must first adhere to the vessel walls and then change their shape and slither through the wall itself before they are active in the body's defense. A decrease in adherence of the cells available to venipuncture would indicate either decreased readiness, or that the cells had already responded by attaching to the walls and/or leaving the blood stream to move toward the site where their action was required.

(3) Cellular shape (SC). As mentioned above, the cells must be able to change shape in order to exit the blood stream. The ability to change shape is also required in order to surround the bacteria or other target of attack.

The Methods

After several pilot studies, the investigators conducted four replications of their basic design, with moderate refinements. The general pre-post design involved the following segments: (1) During the first session, blood was drawn, consent form signed, psychological scales administered, and blood was drawn again. The blood work was considered a control sample. (2) The final session constituted the experimental condition: blood was drawn, the imagery session was conducted, and blood taken again. The procedure was double blind in the sense that the person taking the blood was unaware of the actual experimental condition taking place, and the investigator conducting the imagery session was not made aware of the blood results until after the subjects were run and the imagery rated. All subjects were healthy, and they had been previously screened for any diet or other irregularities which might affect their blood results, including recent intake of drugs or alcohol. The majority were college students: all were invited to participate only if they believed in the possibility that they might be able to influence their blood cells. (This is a critical consideration. Belief in the ability to gain conscious control over the physical substrate is a prerequisite for effective self-regulation.) Throughout these studies, subjects served as their own controls.

Here is a summary report of the particular methodology for each of the four experiments:

Experiment I. (N = 18). Three experimental conditions were used for each subject: A condition using electromyographic (EMG) biofeedback with electrodes placed on the frontalis muscle; a general relaxation procedure using Bensen's (1975) procedure; and a relaxation technique which included imaging neutrophils increasing adherence, leaving the blood stream and changing shape. No preliminary training was given prior to the experimental sessions. Blood samples were taken before and immediately after the 25-minute imagery procedures (a within-variance design).

Experiment II. (N = 16). The study was conducted over 6-7 weeks and involved the presentation of information on neutrophil function, as well as training in imagery, relaxation, and how these might apply to immunity. Control blood samples for each subject were drawn before and after the first session, during which time this information was presented, providing data for comparison to imagery sessions. On the sixth and final session, blood was drawn, the imagery instructions were given, blood was drawn again, and the subjects were asked to draw a picture of their imagery. The imagery was subsequently rated.

Experiment III. (N = 27). The procedure was identical with Experiment II, except the subjects were asked to practice imaging the neutrophils remaining in the blood stream so they would be available when the blood sample was drawn.

Experiment IV. (N = 16). This study was also identical to Experiment II, except that the subjects were advised to image an *increase* in WBC and a *decrease* in the stickiness of the neutrophils. An increased stickiness of these cells, as well

145

as an increased stickiness of the vessel walls promotes adherence to the walls and encourages shape change and migration to the site of inflammation. A decrease in stickiness would tend to prevent these activities. Subjects from Experiments II and III were unable or unwilling to participate in this study. Those who did try were unable to image such a change, which they considered "unhealthy" based on the previous training. New subjects were recruited and were told that this type of response was helpful in immune response since they were free from disease and this was a way to exercise their immune system.

Results

Experiment I. No significant differences were found in the dependent measures in any of the groups (biofeedback, general relaxation, and imagery of enhanced neutrophil function) when pre- and post-results were analyzed. Major, uncharacteristic shifts were observed when pre- and post-testing was compared, but not in any predictable direction. It was concluded that either lack of imagery training or the stress of the testing procedure may account for these findings.

Experiment II. In this study, the WBC dropped significantly (Multivariate $F (2, 14) = 29.53$; $p < .0001$), with approximately 60% of the neutrophils having left the blood stream. The counts of the other types of white blood cells remained relatively unchanged. Unexpectedly, adherence also dropped ($F (2,14) = 5.62$, $p < .05$). (See Table 16.) It was hypothesized that the most responsive cells had already adhered or had left the blood stream and were unavailable for sampling.

Table 16

NEUTROPHIL FUNCTION TESTS BEFORE AND AFTER A 25-MINUTE RELAXATION-IMAGERY SESSION

	Before	After	Multivariate F-value	P
Total White Blood Count (WBC)	8,200 ± 1,500	6,400 ± 1,300	29.53	.0001
Adherence (Ad)	45 ± 3	28 ± 2	5.63	.05
Chemotactic (SC) (shape change)	91 ± 5	92 ± 6	.02	NS

Experiment III. Unlike Experiment II, the subjects in this study were asked to image the neutrophils remaining in the blood stream until after the second blood sample was drawn. This time, there were no significant changes in WBC, as expected, given the nature of the imagery instructions. There was a significant increase in adherence, as expected. When the results from Experiments II and III were compared statistically, significantly different patterns were revealed for adherence ($F(2, 12) = 16.7, p < .001$), and a significant interaction effect was found for WBC ($F(12, 13) = 45.14, p < .0001$). The results are summarized in Figures 33 and 34.

Experiment IV. Subjects in this study had been asked to image an increase in WBC and a decrease in adherence. No significant differences were found in WBC, but significant decreases in adherence were found ($t = 3.17, p < .01$).

In these researches, the procedure of the Image-CA was modified to be relevant to the imagery of a single cell type (i.e., the neutrophil), and to a situation where disease was not present (Minning, 1981). The imagery was rated on the basis of vividness, shape change, adherence, leaving the blood stream, strength, general feeling, symbolism, and clinical judgment. The imagery ratings were done on subjects in Experiments II, III, and IV, and the significant correlations between the dimensions and blood measures are shown in Tables 17, 18, and 19. As can be observed in Experiment II, several significant correlations between variables were found, but results of the adherence measures were correlated in the opposite direction of the hypothesis—the more effective the imagery was rated, the less the adherence. In Experiment III, where the subjects had been instructed to allow the neutrophils to remain available until the sample was drawn, the correlations were significant and in the predicted direction. The results of Experiment IV, where the effectiveness of imagery was judged to be in the opposite direction of Experiment III (i.e., increase in WBC and decrease in adherence), showed relatively fewer correlations, but the majority were still found with the adherence measure. In this last study, playfulness and "felt sense," or the extent that subjects actually felt something going on inside of their bodies, were also included as dimensions and showed a relationship to blood changes.

147

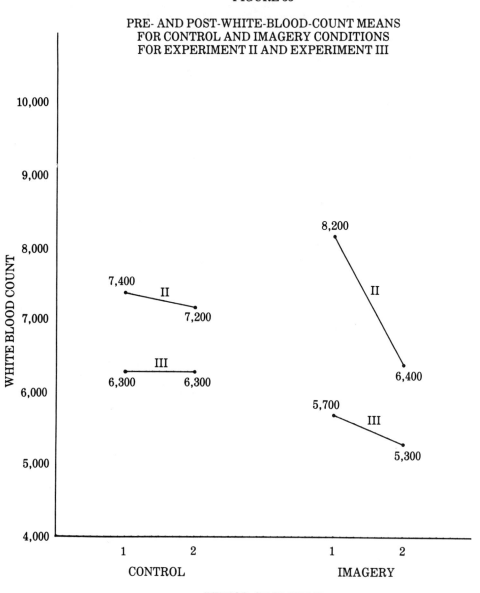

FIGURE 33

PRE- AND POST-WHITE-BLOOD-COUNT MEANS
FOR CONTROL AND IMAGERY CONDITIONS
FOR EXPERIMENT II AND EXPERIMENT III

Experiment II ($n = 16$)
Experiment III ($n = 27$)

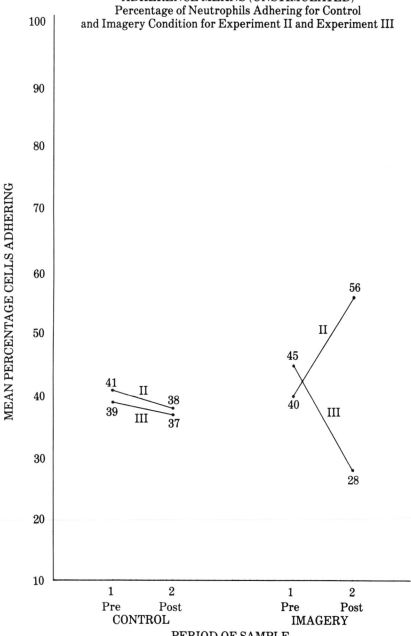

FIGURE 34
ADHERENCE MEANS (UNSTIMULATED)
Percentage of Neutrophils Adhering for Control
and Imagery Condition for Experiment II and Experiment III

Experiment II ($n = 16$)
Experiment III ($n = 27$)

Table 17

Experiment II (↓ WBC ↑ Ad)

SIGNIFICANT CORRELATIONS BETWEEN IMAGERY RATINGS AND PRE TO POST CHANGES IN BLOOD FUNCTION DURING IMAGERY

(n = 16)

IMAGERY CONDITION Blood Function Difference Scores	IMAGERY RATINGS							
	Vividness	Shape Change	Adherence	Leaving the Blood Stream	Strength	General Feeling	Symbolism	Clinical Judgment
White Blood Count (WBC)				.55*			.66**	
Adherence Unstimulated (Ad)	.38	.37			.59**		.36	
Imagery Adherence Stimulated (St. Ad.)		−.67**	−.57**	−.49**	−.44*	−.46*		−.71***

p < .10
*p < .05
**p < .01
***p < .001

NOTE: Blank cells are correlations of less than .35 (p > .10).

Table 18

Experiment III

SIGNIFICANT CORRELATIONS BETWEEN IMAGERY RATINGS AND PRE TO POST CHANGES IN BLOOD FUNCTION DURING IMAGERY

(n = 27)

		IMAGERY RATINGS			
	Vividness	Adherence	Strength	General Feeling	Symbolism	Clinical Judgment
Adherence (Ad), Unstimulated	.41*				.31	
Adherence (St. Ad.), Stimulated	.46**		.52**	.49**	.51**	.41*

p < .10
* p < .05
** p < .01

NOTE: Blank cells are correlations of less than .27 (p > .10).

Table 19

Experiment IV (↑ WBC; ↓ Ad)

SIGNIFICANT CORRELATIONS BETWEEN IMAGERY RATINGS AND PRE TO POST CHANGES IN BLOOD FUNCTIONS DURING IMAGERY

(n = 16)

	VIV	WBC	Ad	Strength	Symb	Felt Sense	Clin. Judg.	Play	Feel
WBC		−.48*	−.39						
Ad	.43	.46*					−.33		
Stim Ad	−.23					−.47*	−.47*	−.50*	

$p < .10$
*$p < .05$

NOTE: Blank cells are correlations of less than .35 ($p > .10$).

Impressions

These carefully controlled studies provide the first substantial experimental support for the potential of imagery as a regulator of immune function. It is clear that at least for one cell type (the neutrophil), and for at least one function of that cell (adherence), selective control is possible. Furthermore, it is difficult to account for the results in terms of a general relaxation hypothesis or a normal maturational or desensitizing effect of the testing situation. In the authors' own concluding words, "These preliminary results are consistent with the hypothesis that relaxation/imagery can be related to changes in neutrophil function. Apparently minor alterations in imagery appear to correspond to major shifts in function of these white blood cells. Effects demonstrated both directional shifts in the adherence of neutrophils which corresponded with the intended imagery." (Schneider, Smith, & Whitcher, 1983, p. 53).

Children's Images as Predictors of Cancer Prognosis

One of the greatest challenges facing health professionals is to find a way to communicate with severely ill children, and to allow them to share their feelings and understanding of the changes in their bodies and lives. Emotions, even for an adult, are at a preverbal level, and it is only with practice that words become attached to feeling states. Getting children to talk out their fears and concerns may be expecting the impossible. On the other hand, images which are also preverbal are closer in both neurological and evolutionary origin to emotions, and would therefore seem to be a good way for children to express the emotionally charged events related to having cancer.

In pilot work with children, we found that absenteeism from school could be predicted on the basis of children's images of the battle between cold germs and their white blood cells. The high-absentee children used weaker images for their defense and drew on 25% or less of the page, while the low-absentee group drew complicated, moralistic, and dynamic figures to represent their white blood cells. In general, the high-absentee children appeared to be overpowered by their illness and unable to influence their self-protection.

Speculating that children with cancer may feel even more overpowered by their disease, particularly if they were in a high-risk category of diagnosis, Sandra Graves (1982) developed a scoring system of the cancer "battle.'

Thirty children diagnosed with malignancy were asked to draw the battle between their cancer and their system of defense against cancer. Graves then identified six dimensions, scoring each on a five-point scale with a "5" indicating significantly more positive imagery of the defense. A "1" was given if the cancer was viewed as winning the battle. The specific dimensions were: (1) size of the objects drawn for cancer and defense; (2) relative number of objects drawn for cancer and the defense; (3) powerfulness of the images used for cancer and the defense; (4) area on the paper used for objects representing cancer and the defense; (5) aggressiveness of objects drawn for cancer and defense; and (6) effectiveness of the cancer and defense in the battle.

Stepwise discriminant function analyses revealed the powerfulness dimension to be the best discriminator between high and low medical risk groups of children with cancer. Five characteristics, in addition to the powerfulness, were found to discriminate independently between extreme risk groups of 12 children with leukemia: The size dimension of the battle drawing, mental age, chronological age, the meaning of cancer as large to small, and the meaning of cancer as dying or living (the latter two items were part of a semantic differential scale Graves devised to help the children verbally describe their condition).

Graves concluded that the data suggest children with malignancies are able to convey the life-threatening nature of their illness, and the awareness is portrayed in their drawings. The drawings are useful in that they provide a measure of the children's understanding of the seriousness of their illness, and a record of their ability to cope. They can also serve as a type of play which may assist in coping, as well as learning to verbalize concerns and misconceptions about the disease, and the difficult treatment most of them undergo.

154

REFERENCES
PART I
IMAGE-CA

Achterberg, J., Lawlis, G. F., Simonton, O. C., & Simonton, S. Psychological factors and blood chemistries as disease outcome predictors for cancer patients. *Multivariate Clinical Experimental Research*, December, 1977.

Achterberg, J., Simonton, O. C., & Matthews-Simonton, S. *Stress, psychological factors and cancer: An annotated bibliography.* Fort Worth: New Medicine Press, 1976.

Allport, G., & Ross, J. Personal religious orientation and prejudice. *Journal of Personality and Social Psychology*, 1967, *5*, 432-443.

Bacon, C. L., Renneker, R., & Cutler, M. A psychosomatic survey of cancer of the breast. *Psychosomatic Medicine*, 1952, *14*, 543.

Bahnson, C. B., & Bahnson, M. B. Cancer as an alternative to psychosis: A theoretical model for somatic and psychologic regression. In D. M. Kissen & L. LeShan (Eds), *Psychosomatic aspects of neoplastic disease.* Philadelphia: Lippincott, 1964, 184. (a)

Bahnson, C. B., & Bahnson, M. B. Denial and repression of primitive impulses and of disturbing emotions in patients with malignant neoplasms. In D. M. Kissen & L. LeShan (Eds), *Psychosomatic aspects of neoplastic disease.* Philadelphia: Lippincott, 1964, 42. (b)

Bahnson, C. B., & Bahnson, M. B. Role of the ego defenses: Denial and repression in the etiology of malignant neoplasm. In E. M. Weyer (Ed.), *Annals of the New York Academy of Sciences*, 1966, *125*(3), 827.

Benson, H. *The relaxation response.* New York: William Morrow, 1975.

Betts, G. H. *The distribution and functions of mental imagery.* Teachers College: Contributions to Education, 1909.

Blumberg, E. M. Results of psychological testing of cancer patients. In J. A. Gengerelli & F. J. Kirkner (Eds), *The psychological variables in human cancer*. Berkeley: University of California Press, 1954, 30.

Booth, G. Cancer and humanism. In D. M. Kissen & L. LeShan (Eds), *Psychosomatic aspects of neoplastic disease*. Philadelphia: Lippincott, 1964, 159.

Brown, B. *New mind, new body*. New York: Harper & Row, 1974.

Bugental, J. F. T. Discussion of E. M. Blumberg's article, Results of psychological testing of cancer patients. In J. A. Gengerelli & F. J. Kirkner (Eds), *The psychological variables in human cancer*. Berkeley: University of California Press, 1954, 95.

Cautela, J. The use of covert conditioning in hypnotherapy. *International Journal of Clinical and Experimental Hypnosis*, 1975, *23*, 15.

Cobb, Beatrix. A socio-psychological study of the cancer patient. Unpublished doctoral dissertation, University of Texas, Austin, 1952.

Coppen, A. J., & Metcalfe, M. Cancer and extraversion. In D. M. Kissen & L. LeShan (Eds), *Psychosomatic aspects of neoplastic disease*. Philadelphia: Lippincott, 1964.

Darwin, C. R. *The origin of the species by means of natural selection, or, the preservation of favored races in the struggle for life* (6th ed.). London: John Murray, 1901.

Ellis, F. W., & Blumberg, E. M. Comparative case summaries with psychological profiles in representative rapidly and slowly progressive neoplastic diseases. In J. A. Gengerelli & F. J. Kirkner (Eds), *The psychological variables in human cancer*. Berkeley: University of California Press, 1954, 72.

Evans, E. *A psychological study of cancer*. New York: Dodd, Mead, 1926.

Evans, R. B., Stern, E., & Marmorston, J. Psychological-hormonal relationships in men with cancer. *Psychological Reports*, 1965, *17*, 715.

Foque, E. Le probleme du cancer dans ses aspects psychiques. *Gaz. Hop. Paris*, 1931, *104*, 827.

Gilman, S. C., Schwartz, J. M., Milner, R. J., Bloom, F. E., & Feldman, J. D. Beta-endorphin enhances lymphocyte proliferative responses. *Proceedings of the National Academy of Science*, 1982, *79*(July), 4226-4230.

Graves, S. L. Children's drawings as predictors of prognosis in cancer. Doctoral dissertation, University of Louisville, Kentucky, 1983.

Greene, W. A. Psychological factors in reticuloendothelial disease. *Psychosomatic Medicine*, 1954, *16*, 220.

Greene, W. A. The psychosocial setting of the development of leukemia and lymphoma. In E. M. Weyer (Ed.), *Annals of the New York Academy of Sciences*, 1966, *125*(3), 794.

Greene, W. A., Young, L., & Swisher, S. M. Psychological factors and reticuloendothelial disease. II. Observations on a group of women with lymphomas and leukemias. *Psychosomatic Medicine*, 1956, *18*, 284.

Hall, H. R. Hypnosis and the immune system: A review with implications for cancer and the psychology of healing. *Journal of Clinical Hypnosis*, 1982-83, *25*(2-3), 92-103.

Hall, H. R., Longo, S., & Dixon, R. Hypnosis and the immune system: The effect of hypnosis on T and B cell function. Paper presented to The Society for Clinical and Experimental Hypnosis, 33rd Annual Workshops and Scientific Meeting, Portland, Oregon, October, 1981.

Hathaway, S. R., & McKinley, J. C. *Minnesota multiphasic personality inventory*. New York: Psychological Corporation, 1943.

Hinkle, L. E., Christenson, W., Benjamin, B., & Wolf, H. G. Observations on the role of nasal adaptive reactions, emotions and life situations in the genesis of minor respiratory illnesses. *Psychosomatic Medicine*, 1962, *24*, 515.

Holt, R. R. Imagery: The return of the ostracized. *American Psychologist*, 1964, *19*, 254-264.

Huckabee, M. Introversion-extroversion and imagery. *Psychological Reports*, 1974, *34*, 453-454.

Inman, O. B. Development of two different types of cancer in a patient undergoing psychoanalytic treatment. In D. M. Kissen & L. LeShan (Eds), *Psychosomatic aspects of neoplastic disease*. Philadelphia: Lippincott, 1964.

Izsak, F. C., & Medalie, J. H. Comprehensive follow-up of carcinoma patients. *Journal of Chronic Disease*, 1971, *24*, 179-191.

Jacobs, J. S. L. Cancer: Host-resistance and host-acquiescence. In J. A. Gengerelli & F. J. Kirkner (Eds), *The psychological variables in human cancer*. Berkeley: University of California Press, 1954, 128.

157

Jacobsen, E. *Progressive relaxation.* Chicago: University of Chicago Press, 1942.

Jung, C. G. *Psychology and alchemy.* Princeton, N.J.: Princeton University Press, 1968.

Khatina, J. Vividness of imagery and creative self-perception. *The Gifted Child Quarterly,* 1975, *19*(1), 33-37.

Kissen, D. M. The significance of personality in lung cancer in men. In E. M. Weyer (Ed.), *Annals of the New York Academy of Sciences,* 1966, *125*(3), 820.

Kissen, D. M. Psychosocial factors, personality and lung cancer in men aged 55-64. *British Journal of Medical Psychology,* 1967, *40,* 29.

Kissen, D. M., & Eysenck, H. J. Personality in male lung cancer patients. *Journal of Psychosomatic Research,* 1962, *6,* 123.

Klopfer, B. Psychological variables in human cancer. *Journal of Projective Techniques,* 1957, *21,* 331-340.

Koenig, R., Levin, S. M., & Brennan, M. J. The emotional status of cancer patients as measured by a psychological test. *Journal of Chronic Disability,* 1967, *20,* 923.

Lamarck, J. *Philosophie zoologique.* Paris: J. B. Balliere, 1830.

Lawlis, G. F., & Lu, E. Judgment of counseling process: Reliability, agreement and error. *Psychological Bulletin,* 1972, *78,* 17-20.

LeShan, L. An emotional life history pattern associated with neoplastic disease. In E. M. Weyer (Ed.), *Annals of the New York Academy of Sciences,* 1966, *125,* 3.

LeShan, L., & Worthington, R. E. Some recurrent life-history patterns observed in patients with malignant disease. *Journal of Nervous and Mental Disease,* 1956, *124,* 460.

Levenson, H. Distinctions within the concept of internal-external control: Development of a new scale. *Proceedings of the American Psychological Association,* 1972, 259-260.

Locke, S. E., & Horning-Rohan, M. *Mind and immunity: Behavioral immunology, an annotated bibliography 1976-1982.* New York: Institute for the Advancement of Health, 1983.

Luria, A. *The mind of a mnemonist.* New York: Basic Books, 1968.

Luthe, W. *Autogenic therapy.* Vol. I-VI. New York: Grune & Stratton, 1969.

Miller, R. F., & Jones, H. W. The possibility of precipitating the leukemia state by emotional factors. *Blood*, 1948, *8*, 880.

Minning, C. Doctoral dissertation, Michigan State University, East Lansing, 1981.

Muslin, H. L., Gyarfas, K., & Pieper, W. J. Separation experience and cancer of the breast. In E. M. Weyer (Ed.), *Annals of the New York Academy of Sciences*, 1966, *125*(3), 802.

Neisser, V. The processes of vision. In A. Richardson (Ed.) *Perception, mechanism and models*. San Francisco: Freeman, 1972.

Nemeth, G., & Mezei, A. Personality traits of cancer patients compared with benign tumor patients on the basis of the Rorschach test. In D. M. Kissen and L. LeShan (Eds), *Psychosomatic aspects of neoplastic disease*. Philadelphia: Lippincott, 1954, 12.

Netzer, M. The body image of women under study for cancer. Unpublished dissertation, Yeshiva University, New York, 1965.

Paget, I. *Surgical pathology*. (2nd ed.) London: Longmons, 1870.

Palmer, R. D., & Field, P. B. Visual imagery and susceptibility to hypnosis. *Journal of Consulting and Clinical Psychology*, 1968, *32*, 456-461.

Paloucek, F. P., & Graham, J. B. The influence of psychosocial factors on the prognosis in cancer of the cervix. In E. M. Weyer (Ed.), *Annals of the New York Academy of Sciences*, 1966, *125*(3), 814.

Paivio, A. Mental imagery in associative learning and memory. *Psychological Review*, 1969, *76*, 241-263.

Peavey, B. S. Biofeedback assisted relaxation: Effects on phagocytic immune function. Doctoral dissertation, North Texas State University, Denton, 1982.

Pelletier, K. R. *Mind as healer, mind as slayer*. New York: Dell, 1977.

Plotnikoff, N. P., Miller, C. G., & Murgo, A. J. From reports at the Second International Conference on Immunopharmacology, Washington, D. C., 1982. Summarized by Treichel, J. A., How brain proteins fight disease. *Science News*, 1982 (July 24), *122*, 55.

Prehn, R. T. The relationship of immunology to carcinogenesis. *Annals of the New York Academy of Science*, 1969, *164*, 449-459.

Reznikoff, M. Psychological factors in breast cancer. *Psychosomatic Medicine*, 1955, *17*, 96.

159

Richardson, A. *Mental imagery*. London: Routledge & Kegan Paul, 1969.

Riley, V. Mouse mammary tumors: Alteration of incidence as apparent function of stress. *Science*, 1975, *189*, 465-467.

Samuels, M., & Samuels, N. *Seeing with the mind's eye*. New York and Berkeley: Random House, 1975.

Schneider, J., Smith, C. S., & Whitcher, S. The relationship of mental imagery to white blood cell (neutrophil) function: Experimental studies of normal subjects. Uncirculated mimeo., Michigan State University, College of Medicine, East Lansing, 1983.

Schultz, W. F. *The FIRO-B scales: Manual.* Palo Alto, Calif.: Consulting Psychologists Press, 1967.

Selye, H. *The stress of life*. New York: McGraw-Hill, 1956.

Sheehan, P. Stimulus imagery effect and the role of imagery in incidental learning. *Australian Journal of Psychology*, 1973, *25*, 93-102.

Simonton, O. C., & Simonton, S. Belief systems and the management of the emotional aspects of malignancy. *Journal of Transpersonal Psychology*, 1975, *7*, 29-47.

Snow, H. L. *Clinical notes on cancer*. London: Churchill, 1883.

Snow, H. L. *The reappearance of cancer after apparent extirpation*. London: Churchill, 1890.

Snow, H. L. *Cancer and the cancer process*. London: Churchill, 1893.

Solomon, G. F., & Amkraut, A. A. Emotions, stress, and immunity. *Frontiers of Radiation Therapeutic Oncology*, 1972, *1*, 84-96.

Tarlau, M., & Smalheiser, I. Personality patterns in patients with malignant tumors of the breast and cervix: An exploratory study. *Psychosomatic Medicine*, 1951, *13*, 117.

Thomas, C. B. Precursors of premature disease and death. *Annals of Internal Medicine*, 1976, *85*, 653-658.

Trestman, R. L. Imagery, coping, and physiological variables in adult cancer patients. Doctoral dissertation, University of Tennessee, Knoxville, 1981.

Wagman, R., & Stewart, C. Visual imagery and hypnotic susceptibility. *Perceptual and Motor Skills*, 1974, *38*, 815-822.

Walshe, W. A. *The nature and treatment of cancer.* London: Taylor and Walton, 1846.

Wheeler, J. P., & Caldwell, B. McD. Psychological evaluation of women with cancer of the breast and of the cervix. *Psychosomatic Medicine,* 1955, *17,* 256.

PART
II
IMAGE-SP

---

*This Part was written in collaboration with C. E. McCoy, Ed.D., David Selby, M.D., and Vert Mooney, M.D.

CHAPTER 5

INTRODUCTION

Pain is difficult to define. The different disciplines have very different descriptions of pain, and each person experiencing pain has his or her own perceptions. For example, behavioral scientists perceive pain as being a message of suffering which combines physical sensation, emotions, and cognitions. Neurologists understand· pain as impulses that stem from sensory inputs. The person in pain experiences the pain as a signal that something is wrong. The pain serves as a warning, much like the red lights on the car dashboard that signal when oil pressure is low.

Pain as a symptom, rather than any disease itself, tends to be the reason that most people seek medical care. Because pain is a highly personalized and subjective experience with many contributing factors, it creates a mixed set of messages that may or may not relate to any actual tissue damage. And therein lies the problem in both measuring and understanding pain as a symptom of disease.

Measuring Pain

There are a number of historical problems in quantifying pain: First, much of the work was done in a laboratory setting where pain was experimentally produced. The results of these analogue studies provided little in the way of understanding clinical pain, especially pain related to chronic disease or disability. Being stuck with a pin or doused in ice water can scarcely be compared to months or years of unrelenting discomfort. Second, the research has been based on the underlying assumption that the pure perception of physical pain could be segmented out from the subjective realization of the pain. This not only reflects outmoded Cartesian thought, but it betrays a basic ignorance of pain pathways and the role of the central nervous system in brain/behavior relationships.

Further, most of the procedures for measuring clinical pain have not been reliable, or are too harmful or too troublesome to be practical. These procedures include correlating pain intensity with neck tension, respiration, finger blood volume, GSR, heart rate, and eye movement (Wolff, 1978); observing pain behaviors such as moaning, restlessness, limping, grimaces, and medication requests (Fordyce, 1976); and using pain-matching techniques. For the latter, the patient is asked to state when experimentally induced discomfort matches his or her own pain. The pain is produced by applying a tourniquet, immersing an extremity in icy water, or by applying electrical stimulation (Hilgard et al., 1974; Wolff, 1978; Sternbach, 1974).

Another approach to the measurement of pain has been to collect verbal impressions of the pain through standardized questionnaires. The most well-known of these is the McGill Pain Questionnaire (Melzack, 1975). It contains 102 adjectives describing pain. The words are divided into categories that have sensory, affective, and evaluative attributes. The main problem with this instrument is that it was standardized on a well-educated sample, many of whom were in the medical field. The words are too difficult for the average person with back injury to understand. (The vast majority of back injuries occur to blue collar workers and are related to the nature of their work.) The questionnaire is inappropriate for subcultures with limited English. Further, the scoring does not take into consideration the cultural and sex bias present in responses (Lawlis, Achterberg, Kenner, & Cedar, in press).

Many investigators have reported success in using scaling methods to objectify the self-report of pain. Beecher (1959) has been credited with introducing the method of asking a patient to estimate pain on some scale (0-7, 0-5, 0-10, 0-100). The scale is verbally anchored, with "0" being no pain, and "100" (or the largest number) meaning intolerable, excruciating pain. These scales have been well tested and their validity demonstrated in both behavioral and pharmacological studies (Gracely, McGrath, & Dubner, 1978).

Visual analogue scales further refine the numerical scales (Scott & Huskisson, 1976). With these, the pain patient is given a line of some length. The ends of the line are anchored with "no pain" and "excruciating pain" or some similar words. The patient is asked to mark where his or her pain falls on the continuum. When the numerical scales are compared with the visual analogue, the latter are usually found to be a superior method of communication. The scaling studies are encouraging and validate the reliability of self-report on the quantitative aspects of pain.

The Image-SP was designed to extend the measurement of pain, particularly pain associated with back injury. This disorder is resistant to treatment, widespread (some estimates suggest it strikes 50% of the population), and the single most costly work-related injury. Because of its chronicity, spinal pain is associated with prescription narcotic addiction, depression, and massive disruptions in career and family life. It is complicated by litigation, health complications from an inactive lifestyle, and, often, by iatrogenic problems from multiple unsuccessful surgeries. Spinal pain is clearly a major health problem in this country.

The Image-SP began as an assessment tool designed by Dr. David Selby, an orthopedic surgeon specializing in spinal pain. A form of pain drawing was used in the Pain Clinic, Los Ranchos Amigos, by Dr. Vert Mooney and his colleagues. Drs. Lawlis, McCoy, Selby, and Mooney used the drawing form in the Spinal Pain Clinic, Dallas Rehabilitation Institute, over a seven-year period. As a result, they revised the form and devised a scoring system.

CHAPTER 6
THE TECHNIQUE

The instrument is a sheet of paper on which a symmetrical human figure is outlined. The patient is asked to draw his or her pain on the areas involved, and to indicate the quality of the pain using specific notation (see Figure 35). Also on the sheet is a five-inch line that serves to record perceived percentage of pain in the back versus the legs. The figure drawing is constructed to allow a grid of one-half inch squares to be placed over the drawing, yielding a way of quantifying the amount of space the person has invested in pain.

ADMINISTRATION OF THE IMAGE-SP*

Before administering the Image-SP, you need to conduct an evaluation asking the patient to describe his or her pain symptoms and any personal methods of pain management. You should also elicit the patient's images and feelings about the pain symptoms, attitudes toward the setting where the injury took place, the family's response, and so forth. The point of the interview is to gather basic information about the nature of events that trigger pain and about any social reinforcers that might be maintaining the pain (Lawlis & McCoy, 1983). The questions in the Image-SP Response Sheet (see Figure 36) give structure to the interview.

---

*For purchase of materials and audiotapes, contact the publisher.

FIGURE 35

IMAGE-SP
Pain Drawing

By David Selby, M.D., C. E. McCoy, Ed.D., and G. Frank Lawlis, Ph.D.

Draw the location of your pain on the body outlines and mark how bad it is on the pain line at the bottom of the page.

ACHE	BURNING	NUMBNESS	PINS & NEEDLES	STABBING	OTHER
AAAA	= = = = =	OOOO	. . . . . .	/ / / / /	x x x x
AA	= = = = =	OO	. . . . . .	/ / / /	x x x

Percentage of pain in back _____ Percentage of pain in legs _____

FRONT   BACK

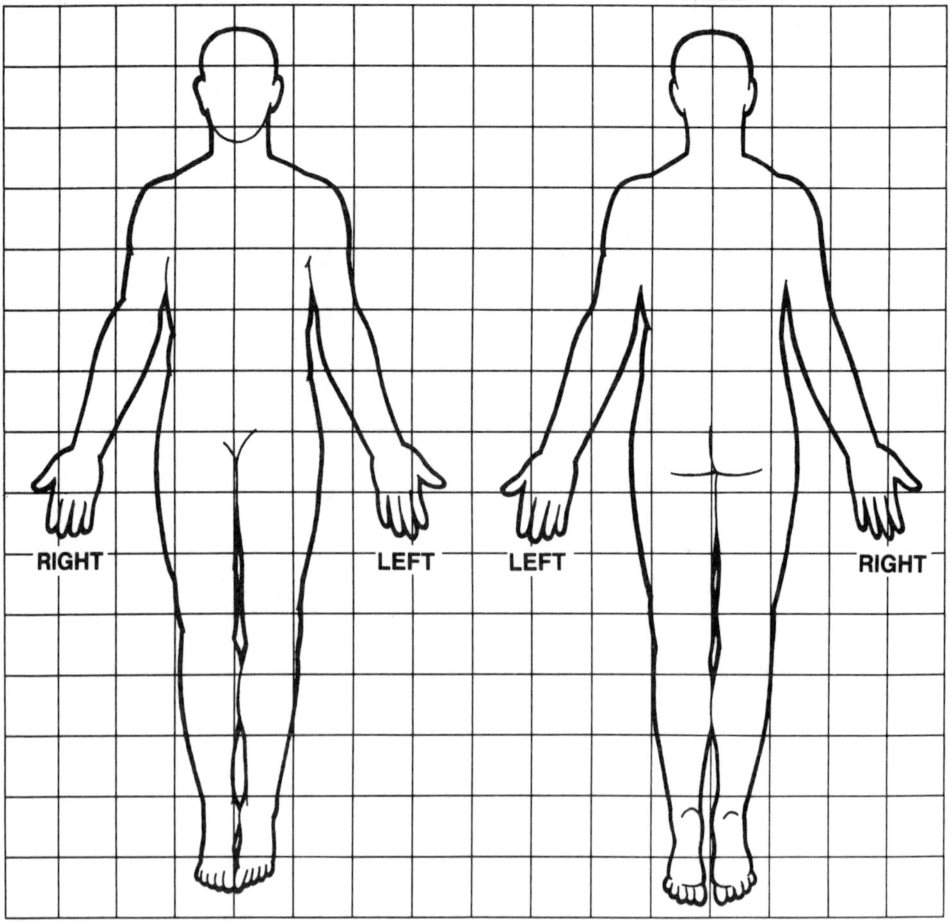

RIGHT   LEFT   LEFT   RIGHT

NO PAIN ⊢————————————————————————————⊣ INTOLERABLE
PAIN

MARK YOUR PAIN ESTIMATE

IMAGE-SP
Response Sheet

Date: _____

Name: _____ Age: _____

Occupation: _____ Employer: _____

Number of years on the job: _____ Date last worked: _____

Date of injury: _____

Describe how injury occurred: _____

_____

When did you first have onset of pain? _____

Mechanism of pain onset: _____ No accident   _____ Bending
_____ Auto accident   _____ Fall
_____ Twisting   _____ Hit in back
_____ Pulling   _____ Other _____

Duration of pain: _____ Less than 1 year   _____ Less than 2 years
_____ Less than 5 years   _____ Less than 10 years
_____ More than 10 years

When does pain occur?   _____ At rest   _____ With working or lifting
_____ Sitting   _____ Less than 8 hours a day
_____ Walking   _____ 8-16 hours a day
_____ All the time   _____ During sexual intercourse

What relieves your pain?   _____ Lying down   _____ Sex   _____ Drugs
_____ Sitting   _____ Rest   _____ Traction
_____ Massage   _____ Heat   _____ Standing
_____ Manipulation   _____ Other _____

	Present	(and Critical)
1. Litigation pending	( )	( )
2. Family role	( )	( )
3. Time in chronic pain greater than 6 months	( )	( )
4. Work history		
a. job satisfaction	( )	( )
b. job demands	( )	( )
c. workers compensation check/pay	( )	( )
d. relationship with company	( )	( )
e. tenure in job	( )	( )
5. Complicating factors (social)	( )	( )
6. Complicating factors (medical)	( )	( )
7. Previous treatment similar to present	( )	( )

FIGURE 36

The Response Sheet also addresses several aspects of the social setting that may impede progress and so should be evaluated: pending litigation, role in the family, duration of chronic pain, work history information, medical or social complications, and any previous treatment failures. Check those problems that are present, and indicate in the second column whether they are believed to be critical to recovery. These issues are broadly discussed in the pain literature and will be treated only briefly here.

1. Pending litigation: Litigation may become a serious impediment to recovery, especially if the patient perceives (usually unrealistically, given the statistics) the proverbial pot of gold at the end of the proceedings.

2. Role in the family: Motivation to actively take part in rehabilitation may be impaired if the pain patient has adopted the family role of victim, or of the passive, helpless family member who needs constant care.

3. Duration of chronic pain: The length of time the person has experienced pain is an important factor in recovery. If the pain has lasted for some time, the patient may well have forgotten how a healthy person behaves. Releasing the pain could then threaten the status quo of his or her lifestyle.

4. Work history: The items listed under work history (job satisfaction, job demands, pay, relationship with company, and tenure) should be checked if problems are noted in those areas. Certainly, the patient's relationship with the company relates to his or her motivations to become free of pain and able to work.

5. Social complications: The more stressful events the person associates with or blames on the pain, the poorer the prognosis. These may include marital problems, emotional lability, and lowered tolerance for the hassles of daily living.

6. Medical complications: The person may have sustained other injuries at the same time as the back injury, or may have other coexisting medical problems such as cancer,

hypertension, ulcers, etc. Medications should be listed, as there might be a number of prescriptive drug problems. For example, high doses of muscle relaxants, tranquilizers, and barbiturates might have depressive effects. Long-term drug administration has a detrimental effect on motivation, energy level, and mental alertness. And, of course, there is the concern about addiction with the use of narcotics.

7. Previous treatments: Any modality that has failed once is not likely to prove successful the second or third time around. Previous treatments indicate that there have been previous treatment failures, or else the condition would have improved.

After gathering this information, ask the patient to draw his or her pain in the following manner.

"You see a picture of a front and back of a human body. What I want you to do is close your eyes and relax." (Extra relaxation techniques can be introduced here.) "As you are relaxing, I want you to go on a mental journey through your body and find your pain. If it travels, go with it. Try to understand what kind of pain it is. Is it an ache, a stabbing, a burning, pins and needles, or a numbness? Do not try to remember old pain, just how you feel right now." (Pause.)

"Now with your pencil or pen, draw in the pain you discovered you feel today. See the symbols at the top of the page for the different kinds of pain: ache, burning, numbness, pins and needles, stabbing, and others. Use them to draw your pain." (Pause while the patient draws the pain.)

"Very good. Now tell us what percentage or amount of your pain is in your back and then what percentage is in your legs." (After the responses, these should be written on the protocol.)

"See the line at the bottom of the page. Think of it as a gauge. At one end there is no pain. At the other end is intolerable pain, pain no one could stand. Please indicate how intense your pain is on this line."

173

(After response): "Thank you for your cooperation. Are there questions you wish to ask me at this time or something else you wish to tell me about your condition?"

SCORING AND EVALUATING THE IMAGERY

There are two methods of scoring the pain drawing. One determines the affective components of pain. This scoring method follows from and affirms the results of an earlier study by Ransford, Cairns, and Mooney (1976). They used the drawing to determine whether a pain symptom was organic or functional. The second scoring method predicts treatment response. Use a form like that presented in Figure 37 to summarize the scoring of the pain drawing.

Affective Component

To test the affective component of pain, score the drawing for the following kinds of "unreal" pain (i.e., pain that does not follow any known neurological pathway or that is not believed to be associated with spinal pain of any specified etiology). Assign two points for (a) total leg pain, (b) lateral whole leg pain, (c) circumferential thigh pain, (d) bilateral tibial pain. Assign two points for (a) circumferential foot pain, (b) bilateral foot pain, (c) back pain radiating to iliac crest, groin, or anterior perineum, (d) anterior knee pain, and (e) anterior ankle pain.

Give an extra point each for pain that is dramatized by the following: (a) additional explanatory notes on the pain drawing, (b) pain drawn outside the body outline, (c) circling the painful areas, (d) lines or arrows or other indications to demarcate the painful areas. An additional one point each is given for exaggeration of other areas besides the spine, such as upper trunk, neck, and head. When pain lacks specificity, is vague and amorphous (the "roving pain"), assign one point for small areas, and two points for large. Areas are considered large if they cover more than 1/5 or 20% of the body.

For the affective component, a patient's typical response would be zero, meaning that none of the affective or

IMAGE-SP

Pain Drawing Summary

Affective Notation	**Neurological Notation**	**Probable Diagnosis**

Affective Notation

1. Total Leg (2)
2. Lateral Whole (2)
   Leg Pain
3. Circumferential Leg (2)
4. Bilateral Tibial (2)
5. Circumferential Foot (2)
6. Bilateral Foot (2)
7. Back to Iliam Crest (2)
   Groin, Ant. Perineum
8. Anterior Knee (2)
9. Anterior Ankle (2)
10. Additional Explanation (1)
11. Drawing Outside Body (1)
12. Circling (1)
13. Arrows / Lines (1)
14. Exaggeration (1 pt. each outside spine)
14. Roving (1)

_____

3 or more points are significant

Affective pain score _____

Number of grids _____
    (15 or more indicates multiple causes)

Pain Intensity _____

Neurological Notation

1. _____
2. _____
3. _____
4. _____

Probable Diagnosis

1. _____
2. _____
3. _____

Treatment Plan

1. _____
2. _____
3. _____

Notes: _____

FIGURE 37

psychological aspects would be incorporated in the pain symptom. A score of 3 or more would indicate evidence of significant psychological influence.

Prediction of Treatment Response

The second method of scoring the pain drawing predicts treatment response and is related to psychological profiles. It involves quantifying the amount of space used for the drawing. Use a grid overlay and count the number of one-half inch squares that contain any mark representing pain. This includes lines, words, and other notations as well as the requested pain drawing. The number of squares involved in the patient's notation on the visual analogue scale are included in the grid count also.

CHAPTER 7

STANDARDIZATION AND RESEARCH WITH THE TECHNIQUE

In practice, the total obtained score has ranged from 1 to 55, with the average being 10. The critical cutoff for significant behavioral components is 15. This will be discussed further in the section on Clinical Observations.

Reliability

Reliability estimates for the two scoring systems were based upon interrater agreement and consistency. The affective scoring system had a reliability between two raters of .85, in evaluating 125 subjects. The grid counting system resulted in consistency at the .97 level, with a group of 318 subjects.

Validity

The score on the Image-SP has been correlated with other measures. One study included 25 low-back-pain patients, divided according to their MMPI profiles. Eleven patients were classified as "normal," as their scale elevations on the MMPI were all within the average range. Fourteen of the patients were considered to be "abnormal" in that they had at least one MMPI scale score outside of the average range. Of the so-called "normals," 89% had drawings with 11 or fewer squares containing pain notations. Only 28% of the "abnormals" had drawings of fewer than 11 squares. Seventy-one percent of the people who had abnormal pain drawings had marked on at least 12 or more of the squares. Overall, about 82% of correct classification (i.e., "normal" vs. "abnormal," based upon the MMPI) could be made by counting the number of squares ($x^2 = 8.06, p < .0005$).

These results seem to indicate that the more grids colored in, the more likely the patient will show abnormality on the MMPI, thus the more likely psychopathology.

A second study correlated physicians' ratings of the outcome of surgical and rehabilitation procedures with the number of squares marked on the grid. The physicians provided a global outcome rating based on a composite of pain behaviors, functional criteria (particularly range of motion), and whether the patient had returned to work. Those with a poor composite outcome were assessed a "1," and those with an excellent outcome, a "3." A "2" represented an average outcome. The doctors rated 318 patients who had undergone chemonucleolysis, laminectomy, spinal fusion, spinal pain rehabilitation programs, and/or facet injection. Those who had fewer squares filled in on their pain drawing accounted for 88% of the people in the best outcome category ("3"). Of those with poor outcome, 44% had marked on 15 or more squares ($x^2 = 73.06, p < .001$).

Dr. Vert Mooney, now Chairman of the Division of Orthopedic Surgery at Southwestern Medical School, conducted a predictive study, providing perhaps the most compelling evidence. In the study, the pain drawing was administered before interventions such as spinal fusion, facet injections, and a spinal pain rehabilitation program. The pre-intervention pain drawing predicted to a significant degree the impact of several of the interventions. As can be observed in Table 20, all correlations except those for chemonucleolysis and laminectomy were significant at least at the .05 level. Results were based upon outcome ratings of poor (little or no change following intervention), fair (some improvement), and excellent (improvement expected based upon the procedure). These results are depicted in Figures 38 through 42.

Table 20

CORRELATIONS OF OUTCOME RATINGS
AND DRAWING SCORES

	N	r	p
Chemonucleolysis	30	.300	N.S.
Laminectomy	23	.379	N.S.
Operative Patients	35	.331	$< .05$
Spinal Fusion	54	.531	$< .01$
Spinal Pain Clinic	58	.489	$< .01$
Facet Injections	118	.404	$< .01$

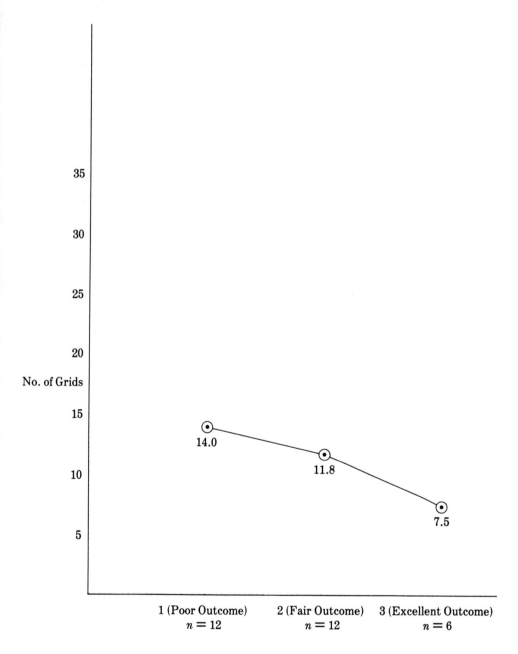

FIGURE 38. QUANTIFICATION OF PAIN DRAWINGS FROM 30 PATIENTS
UNDERGOING CHEMONUCLEOLYSIS

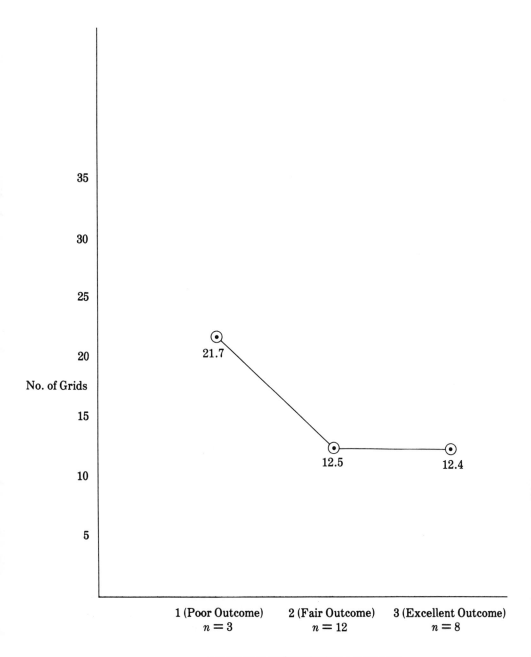

No. of Grids

1 (Poor Outcome)
$n = 3$

2 (Fair Outcome)
$n = 12$

3 (Excellent Outcome)
$n = 8$

POST-TREATMENT EVALUATION

FIGURE 39. QUANTIFICATION OF PAIN DRAWINGS FROM 23 PATIENTS
UNDERGOING LAMINECTOMY

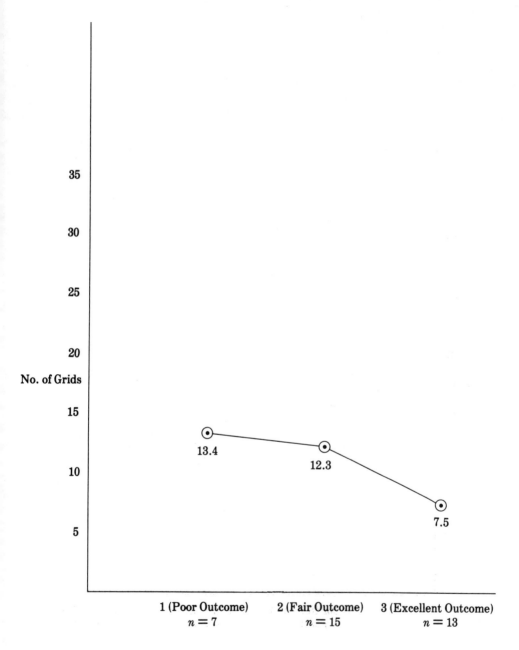

POST-TREATMENT EVALUATION

FIGURE 40. QUANTIFICATION OF PAIN DRAWINGS FROM 35 OPERATIVE
PATIENTS WITH LOW BACK PAIN

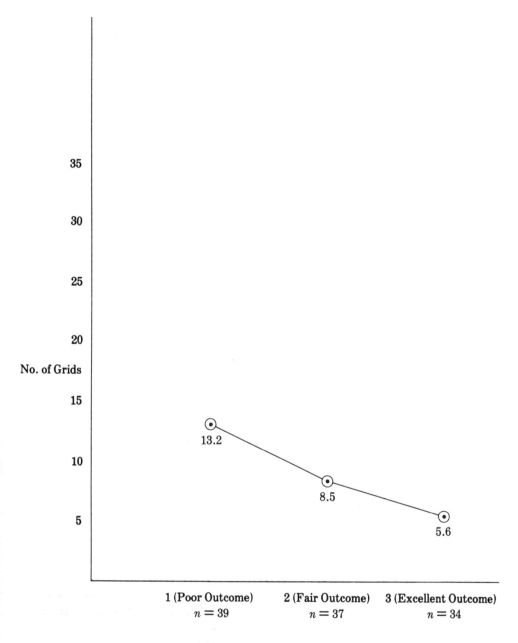

POST-TREATMENT EVALUATION

FIGURE 41. QUANTIFICATION OF PRETREATMENT PAIN DRAWINGS
FROM 110 PATIENTS WITH LOW BACK PAIN UNDERGOING FACET OR
EPIDURAL INJECTION

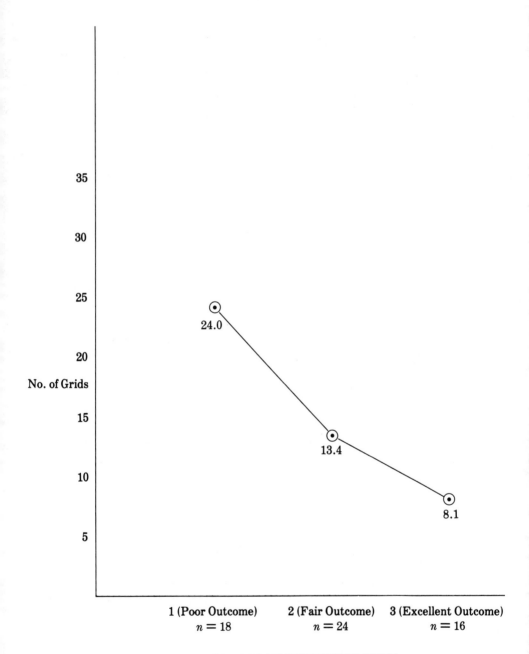

POST-TREATMENT EVALUATION

FIGURE 42. QUANTIFICATION OF PRETREATMENT PAIN DRAWINGS IN
58 PATIENTS WITH LOW BACK PAIN ENTERING SPINAL PAIN CLINIC

CHAPTER 8
CASE STUDIES

On the following pages, three case studies illustrate how the pain drawing relates to psychological profiles and treatment outcome.

1. The first case is presented in Figures 43 and 44. This woman presented herself to the orthopedic surgeon for evaluation. Her drawing covered six squares. She estimated her pain as a "4" and had no other complicating factors. The MMPI scales were not elevated above a T-score of 70, although there was a slight elevation on the Hysteria scale.

   Her treatment involved a spinal fusion, which resulted in an excellent response. One year after treatment, she has no pain, and is fully functioning in her job.

FIGURE 43. CASE STUDY #1

MMPI Profile

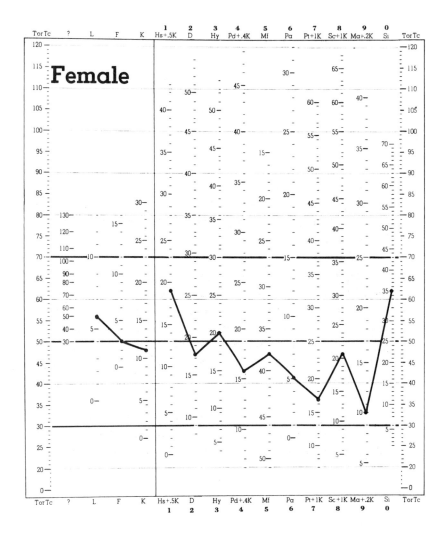

FIGURE 44. CASE STUDY #1

Pain Drawing

DATE: _____   NAME: _____

Please draw where your pain is.

Percentage of pain in back __*80%*__   Percentage of pain in legs __*20%*__

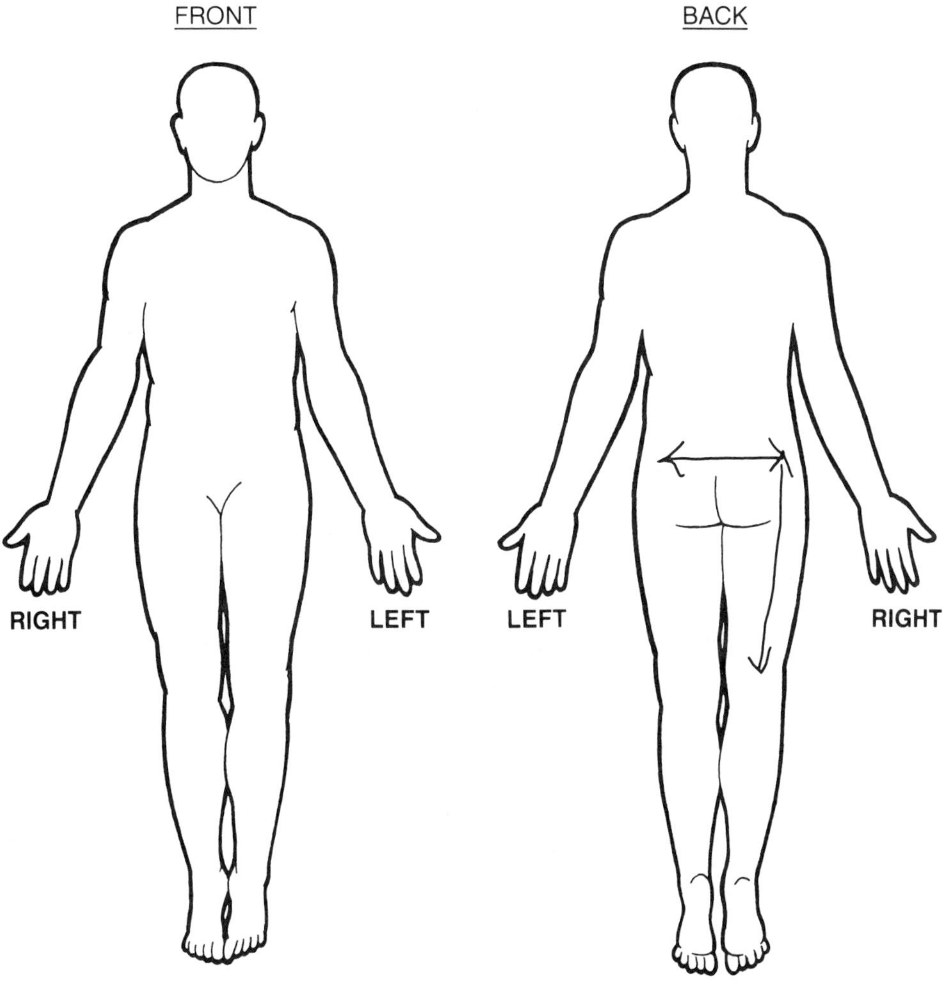

<u>FRONT</u>   <u>BACK</u>

RIGHT   LEFT   LEFT   RIGHT

NO PAIN ├──────────────X─────────────────────┤ INTOLERABLE
         MARK YOUR PAIN ESTIMATE   **PAIN**

2. The next case study is a male whose pain drawing is presented in Figure 46. His drawing filled in 21 grids, and he estimated his pain to be about 9 on a scale of 0-10. His explanation of his pain symptoms was quite involved. His MMPI was interpreted as indicative of significant psychological or other overtones related to pain behavior. As can be seen in Figure 45, three scales (Depression, Hypochrondriasis, and Hypomania) were above the T-score of 70.

FIGURE 45. CASE STUDY #2

MMPI Profile

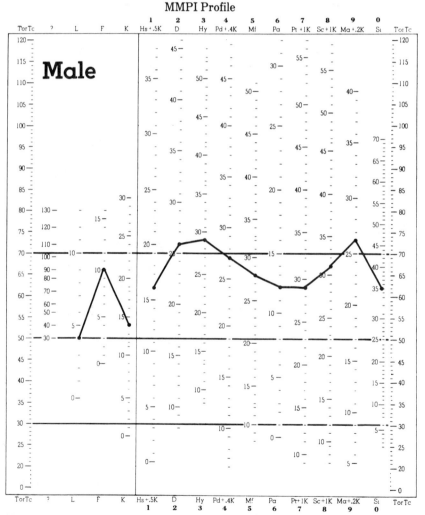

FIGURE 46. CASE STUDY #2

Pain Drawing

DATE: _____ NAME: _____

Draw the location of your pain on the body outlines and mark how bad it is on the pain line at the bottom of the page.

ACHE	BURNING	NUMBNESS	PINS & NEEDLES	STABBING	OTHER
AAAA	= = = = =	○○○○	· · · · · ·	/ / / / /	× × × ×
AA	= = = = =	○○	· · · · · ·	/ / / /	× × ×

Percentage of pain in back _____ Percentage of pain in legs _____

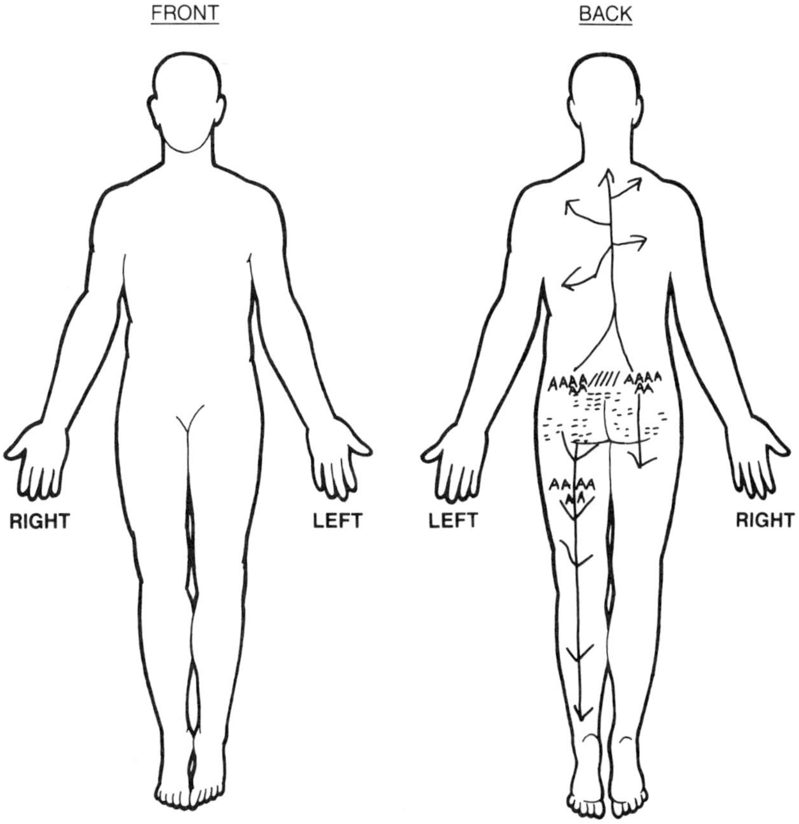

FRONT   BACK

RIGHT   LEFT   LEFT   RIGHT

NO PAIN ├────────────────────────────────X───┤ INTOLERABLE PAIN

MARK YOUR PAIN ESTIMATE

This man was recommended for two interventions, fusion and rehabilitation, which he did not receive. He continued to have pain for a lengthy period of time, although it did subside to the extent that he returned to work. He is periodically seen for pain management.

3. The third case study is presented in Figures 47 and 48. His drawing covered 36 squares on the grid; his estimated pain was 9 on the 0-10 scale. He indicated that 100% of his pain was in his back and 100% was in his legs (obviously, a misunderstanding of the concept of percentage).

FIGURE 47. CASE STUDY #3

MMPI Profile

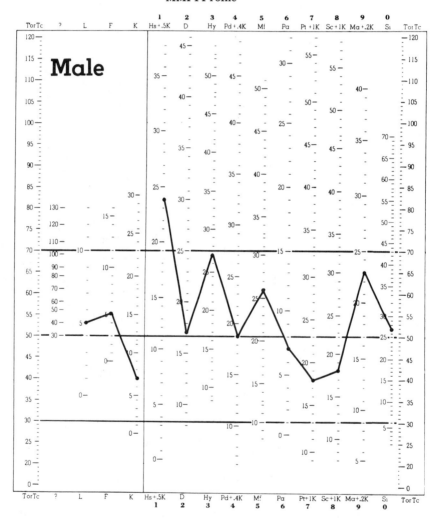

FIGURE 48. CASE STUDY #3

Pain Drawing

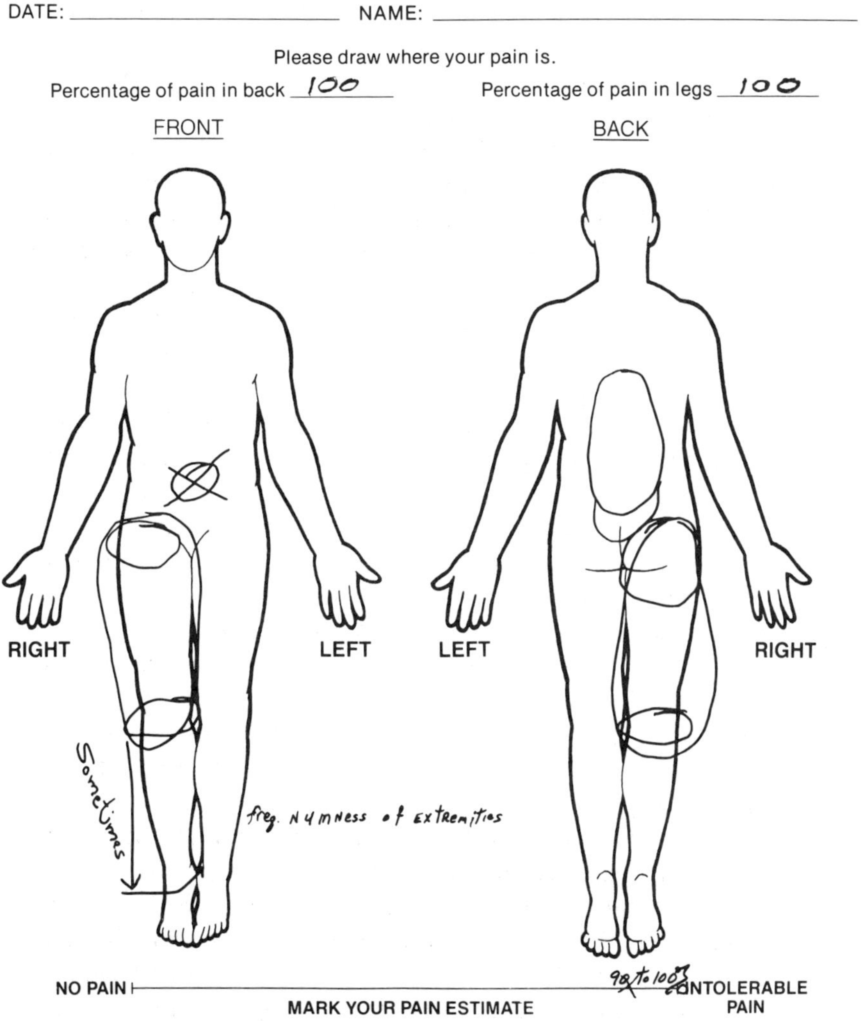

DATE: _____ NAME: _____

Please draw where your pain is.

Percentage of pain in back __*100*__   Percentage of pain in legs __*100*__

<u>FRONT</u>   <u>BACK</u>

RIGHT   LEFT   LEFT   RIGHT

Sometimes

freq. Numness of extremities

NO PAIN ├─────────────────────────────────── *98 to 100%* ─ INTOLERABLE PAIN

MARK YOUR PAIN ESTIMATE

On the MMPI profile, the Hypochondriasis, Hysteria, and Hypomania scales were significantly elevated. The man was given a laminectomy and intensive rehabilitation. He is presently unemployed and has sought medical help from at least six other orthopedic surgeons during the past year. Currently, the medical diagnosis reveals no obvious pathological processes. However, problems with litigation and his workers' compensation settlement continue.

191

CLINICAL OBSERVATIONS

A very complex pain drawing that encompasses a large number of squares may either imply psychopathology or significant, complicated pathology where two or more physical problems coexist. The patient may draw in headache pain which is totally unrelated in etiology to the back pain. Or sciatic pain may be present which can radiate down one or both legs. In either case, large numbers of squares would be used. The meaning of the pain drawing must be drawn from the medical and psychological workup. However, the predictive validity of the measure in terms of treatment response would be expected to hold, regardless of the reason for the complex drawing.

The issue of distinguishing "real" pain from "fake" pain is complex. Patients' versions of their pain are influenced by their attempts to manipulate economic or social factors through their behavior. There is no doubt that motivational issues function in pain symptomology. Typically, motivational issues may be relevant when the patient does not respond to traditional treatment in due time. We can account for this in at least three ways: (1) the patient is rewarded for disease behavior either economically or socially, (2) the patient is using pain for psychological defenses, perhaps to deny or avoid dealing with troublesome feelings or events by focusing on or blaming the pain, and/or (3) the patient has adopted inappropriate habits in coping with pain stimuli, thus producing additional and confusing pain.

The point is that it is difficult to ascertain the specific combination of factors within a brief time. The best that any instrument can achieve is to separate those cases with simple, clear-cut symptoms from those with a complex pain response. Image-SP does discriminate those with exaggerated or complicated symptoms that may stem from either emotional problems or from multiple physical causes. Consider the following case study:

Kay was a 35-year-old female who had a job-related injury that was caused by picking up boxes of produce. Her pain drawing in Figure 49 shows pain throughout her posterior

FIGURE 49. CASE STUDY WITH COMPLEX PAIN RESPONSE

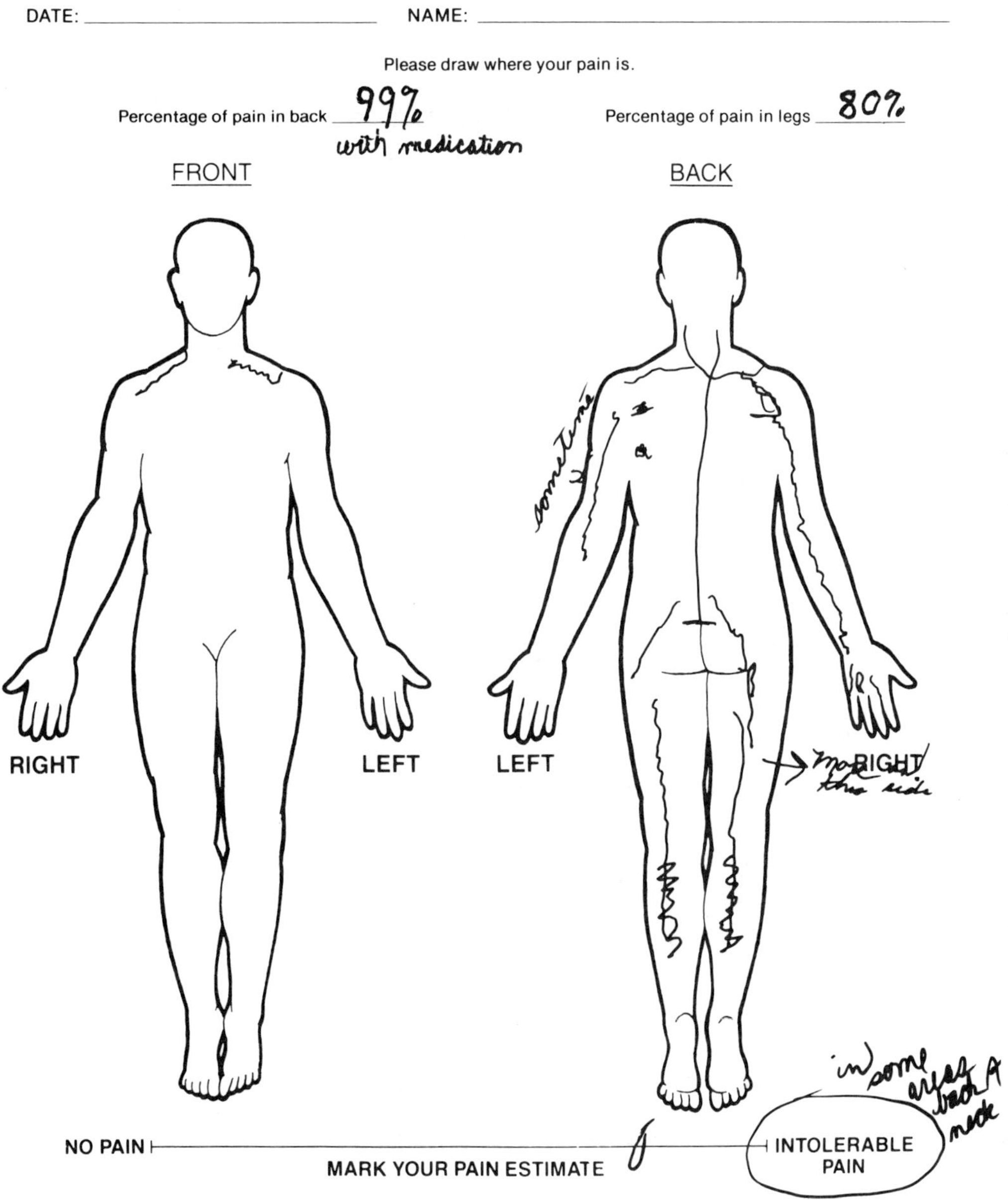

DATE: _____ NAME: _____

Please draw where your pain is.

Percentage of pain in back __99%__
with medication

Percentage of pain in legs __80%__

FRONT

BACK

RIGHT   LEFT   LEFT   *more RIGHT this side* →RIGHT

sometimes

in some areas of back & neck

NO PAIN ├─────────────────────────────────┤ INTOLERABLE PAIN

MARK YOUR PAIN ESTIMATE

body. The number of grids exceeds the norm of 10 (her score being 31). The drawings and writing outside the body of her pain would predict some significant psychological factors in her pain symptoms.

Examiner (Ex): Tell me about your drawing so that I can understand how you feel.

Kay: I just hurt all over. I can't walk very long without it killing me. I think I am going to die. I wish I could die.

Ex: Where do you hurt the most?

Kay: I think in my shoulders, but then when they are easy my back and legs hurt (begins to cry).

Ex: You have over 100% pain, 99% and 80% in your drawing. Would you explain this for me?

Kay: When you hurt the way I hurt, you would understand that when my back hurts, it travels throughout my body. When my legs hurt, they hurt most of my body.

Ex: Let us think about "if" part of your pain was dissolved, what would you want to do with the rest of your life?

Kay: I would go back to work. I have to work to support my family and horses. I don't think they would take me back at the grocery store, but I could find a job.

Ex: Show me what portion of the pain or percentage with which you could work so that we can set some goals.

Kay: I think that I could work with about 30% of my pain, as long as it would not get worse.

Ex: Would it be important for any part of you to hurt less than any other?

Kay: No, just less pain overall.

Kay was referred to the Pain Clinic for evaluation. Based upon her complaints of extreme pain with some classical symptoms of disc disruption syndrome, the surgeons were considering aggressive surgery as a primary intervention. As part of the full evaluation, the Image-SP was included. The findings on her X-ray, CT-scan, and myelogram showed no abnormalities. Her biofeedback records showed extremely high EMG readings (30+ microvolts), indicating a great deal of muscle spasm throughout her back and neck area. The rehabilitation program was very beneficial for Kay. Following a program that emphasized stress management, her pain symptoms were reduced to zero. She had two episodes of intractable pain while in the program, one from the effects of a night-long dancing spree and the other from a hot tub party (she stayed in the tub for eight hours). She has since returned to work in the field of cosmetology. She has learned to manage her symptoms by pacing herself and by reducing the anxiety which provoked her high levels of muscle tension.

SUMMARY

The pain drawing offers a direct communication between health care professional and patient. The symptomatology can be dramatized, and the psychological and neurological aspects more clearly determined. Unfortunately, the scoring does not make specific psychological diagnosis possible (only that some pathology is present), nor has a "malingering" type of drawing been identified to date. Therefore, we suggest that the clinician incorporate the pain drawing within a battery of tests rather than depend solely upon the imagery for a psychological diagnosis. However, the Image-SP does offer predictability concerning response to medical and rehabilitation treatment of spinal pain. This information has never been consistently available from either medical or psychological diagnosis.

REFERENCES
PART II
IMAGE -SP

Beecher, K. K. *Measurement of subjective responses.* New York: Oxford Univ. Press, 1959.

Fordyce, W. E. *Behavioral methods for chronic pain and illness.* St. Louis: Bosby, 1976.

Gracey, R. H., McGrath, P., & Dubner, R. Ratio scales of sensory and affective verbal pain description. *Pain*, 1978, *5*, 5-18.

Hilgard, E., Ruch, J. C., Louge, A. F., Lenox, J. R., Morgan, A. H., & Sachs, L. B. The psychophysics of cold pressor pain and its modification through hypnotic suggestion. *American Journal of Psychology*, 1974, *87*, 17-32.

Lawlis, F., Achterberg, J., Kenner, L., & Cedar, K. Racial and sex differences in pain perception for spinal patients. *Spine*, in press.

Lawlis, F., & McCoy, E. Psychological evaluation of chronic pain patients: The pain drawing grid. Paper given at the American Psychological Association, Los Angeles, CA, 1983.

Melzack, R. The McGill Pain Questionnaire. *Pain*, 1975, *1*, 277-299.

Mooney, V. *Predicted pain levels by drawings.* Unpublished manuscript, 1984.

Ransford, A. O., Cairns, D., & Mooney, V. The pain drawing as an aid to the psychological evaluation of patients with low back pain. *Spine*, 1976, *2*, 127-135.

Scott, J., & Huskisson, E. C. Scaling methods of pain responses. *Pain*, 1976, *3*, 175-184.

Sternbach, R. A. *Pain patients: Traits and treatment.* New York: Academic Press, 1974.

Wolff, B. B. Behavioral measurement of pain. In R. Sternbach (Ed.), *The psychology of pain* (pp. 129-168). New York: Raven Press, 1978.

PART III
IMAGE-DB

*This Part was written in collaboration with Dr. Larry Stevens, Oklahoma University Medical School.

CHAPTER 9

INTRODUCTION

Diabetes mellitus is a chronic disease of metabolism, in which the body is unable to use and regulate proteins, fats, and carbohydrates. The symptoms of diabetes are generally considered to result from a decrease in production of usable pancreatic insulin. Insulin facilitates the transport of glucose and amino acids across the cell membrane. Diabetics, because they do not have enough insulin to aid in the transport, typically have an excess of glucose in the blood and usually have sugar in the urine. Because the body cells are energy-starved, they resort to breaking down stored fats and proteins. Therefore, diabetics also may have elevated levels of free fatty acids in their blood as well. In essence, the body is in a persistent "fasting" state. The symptoms of diabetes mellitus may include abnormal thirst, increased urination, genital itching, and loss of weight and strength. Complications of this disorder are numerous and varied, affecting the entire homeostatic system of the body.

The increased food intake associated with obesity may cause maturity-onset diabetes. According to this hypothesis, increased eating may lead to the secretion of too much insulin. The excessive insulin then acts through a negative-feedback system to reduce the number of target cell insulin receptors, thus making the cells less responsive to available insulin and less capable of using available glucose.

Juvenile-onset diabetes, on the other hand, may have an entirely different cause. This disease involves a marked lack of pancreatic beta cells (often to less than 10% of normal).

Beta cells are on the pancreas and are responsible for insulin production. The diabetic's lack of beta cells results in hypoinsulinemia, hyperglycemia, lipolysis, and ketoacidosis.

An additional causative factor, omitted from many diabetes sourcebooks but receiving widespread consideration from current researchers, is life stress. That stress plays a role in the etiology and course of medical disorders is not a novel concept. Indeed, the development of psychosomatic medicine as a formal area of study in medicine and in psychology reflects the widespread effects of environmental stress on physical disorders. In the field of diabetes research, Cannon, Shohl, and Wright (1911) early demonstrated the occurrence of glycosuria in cats under stress. Folin, Dennis, and Smillie (1914) observed similar effects in people. Since then, a number of authors have reported observed associations between stress and the exacerbation of the diabetic condition (Daniels, 1936; Dunbar, 1943; Menninger, 1935; Meyer, Bollmeyer, & Alexander, 1945). However, these anecdotal presentations failed to adequately control for altered or abandoned therapeutic regimens, which led Rosen and Lidz (1949) to dismiss such claims as secondary to changes in medication-diet-exercise management.

Hinkle and his coworkers (Hinkle, Conger, & Wolf, 1950; Hinkle, Evans, & Wolf, 1951; Hinkle & Wolf, 1952) have investigated the stress-diabetes relationship. They conducted a series of studies that controlled for medication, diet, and exercise levels. The research focused on the direct effects of life stress (induced via instructions to verbally rehearse stressful life events during psychotherapy) on urine glucose, blood glucose, ketone levels, and fluid balance for both diabetic and nondiabetic subjects ($N = 64$). Hinkle, Conger, and Wolf (1950) reported marked incremental and decremental fluctuations in the levels of ketone bodies and of glucose in venous blood for both diabetic and nondiabetic subjects exposed to cognitive life stress, but a greater magnitude of response for diabetic patients. Diabetics showed a general elevation in venous blood ketones after stress. Moreover, these authors cited an anecdotal review of the life histories of more than 50 diabetic patients, reporting that "in nearly all of these cases, the onset of the disorder occurred after a period of environmental and interpersonal stress" (Hinkle & Wolfe, 1952, p. 566).

A more recent series of studies conducted by Vandenbergh and colleagues has lent support to Hinkle et al., but has raised some bemusing questions as well (Vandenbergh, Sussman, & Titus, 1966; Vandenbergh, Sussman, & Vaughan, 1967). These authors used two approaches to induce stress in diabetic subjects and then assessed blood glucose, urine glucose, ketone levels, and fluid balance. The first approach used hypnotic imagery of prior life stresses previously identified by each subject (Vandenbergh, Sussman, & Titus, 1966). The second approach utilized a physical-anticipatory, shock-escape stress paradigm (Vandenbergh, Sussman, & Vaughan, 1967). Otherwise, the studies were identical, with the exception of the addition of a nondiabetic control group in the physical-anticipatory stress design. Both studies demonstrated significant decreases in blood glucose levels from nonstress to stress conditions in diabetic patients but not in controls, nonsignificant increases in plasma-free fatty acids in diabetic patients and in nondiabetic controls, and nonsignificant increases in urinary volume for all groups, without a change in urinary glucose excretion. Increases in plasma-free fatty acids and in urinary volume are consistent with the trends reported by Hinkle and his colleagues. However, the observed decrease in blood glucose levels without a subsequent increase in urinary glucose is contradictory to expected results. Vandenbergh et al. hypothesized (1) that an increased use of glucose in peripheral tissue occurred under the stress conditions, depleting existing glucose supplies and (2) that for insulin-treated diabetics, minor muscle movements produced greater glucose use than in nondiabetics.

Studies that have followed Hinkle and Vandenbergh have by and large been single case reports and correlational studies. Most support Hinkle's contention that emotional stress serves as a triggering mechanism to set off or to exacerbate diabetes in the constitutionally predisposed person. For example, Hong and Holmes (1973) reported a case of diabetes mellitus onset in a Korean physician who had immigrated to the U.S. and experienced major life stress due to cultural changes. Slawson, Flynn, and Kollar (1963) pre-

203

sented post hoc case history studies involving 25 diabetic subjects and reported that 20 of the 25 patients had experienced life stress due to a personal loss, occurring from 1 to 48 months prior to disease detection.

Grant, Kyle, Teichman, and Mendels (1974) improved on prior case studies by attempting to standardize the degree of life stress by using a revision of the Holmes and Rahe Schedule of Recent Events (SRE) life change units (Holmes & Rahe, 1967). Thirty-seven patients were evaluated by a blind rater on a global physical health continuum, and these ratings were correlated with SRE life events. A trend associating life experience, specifically undesirable life events, with changes in diabetic symptomatology was reported, although actual correlations were nonsignificant. A number of design problems were mentioned (e.g., small sample, small number of reported life events, problems in the assessment of diabetic condition changes, and subject biases) which appear to bias this study. Improving on the weaknesses of the study, Chase and Jackson (1981) have found significant correlations between stressful life events occurring within the previous three months and serum triglyceride concentrations (a prelude to free fatty acids), percent hemoglobin A1 (a measure of glucose in blood), serum cholesterol values, and serum glucose concentrations in 84 child and adolescent diabetics. Also, Bradley (1979) found stressful life events occurring within the previous 12 months to be significantly correlated with glycosuria, changes in insulin or oral hypoglycemic tablet prescription, and number of clinic visits. The study was based on a sample that included 114 diabetic adolescents and adults. The replicated correlational values reported in these three studies are indeed suggestive of a cause-effect relationship between stress and diabetes symptom management.

Benton (1953) and Simon and Mirsky (1953) have cited other case reports that support stress-related exacerbation of diabetes mellitus.

CHAPTER 10
THE TECHNIQUE

We have used imagery as a strategy for inquiry and therapy with diabetes in clinical practice since 1976, and several versions of an imagery protocol have been independently developed during that period. The format, standardization, and normative data for the work published here were gathered by Larry Stevens (1983).

As in our other imagery diagnostic techniques (Image-CA, Image-SP), this test was designed to elicit the patient's knowledge of and response to the disease, and to serve to inform and redirect false notions about the disease and its impact. The Image-DB uses many modes of communication: the relaxation and educational process in the imagery induction, a drawing of the aspects of disease as seen by the patient, and a structured interview. The drawings, with the information obtained through the interview, are scored on 16 dimensions using five-point scales. These scales are then summed to yield an overall imagery score. The Image-DB was found to be a reliable instrument, and its validity is shown, in part at least, by its correlation to blood glucose levels.

ADMINISTRATION OF THE IMAGE-DB*

Introduce the diabetic person to the procedure and establish initial rapport prior to testing. Then, ask the person to get into a comfortable position. The relaxation and imagery instructions will take approximately 20 minutes. The usual format for administration is to allow the person to listen to a diabetes cassette tape or to read the script aloud to him/her.

*For purchase of materials and audiotapes, contact the publisher.

Then, give the instructions for drawing the components of the imagery. Finally, conduct the structured interview when the drawings are complete.

Relaxation/Imagery Instructions

Transcription of the Diabetes Tape (Achterberg, 1980).

> This is a tape that will help you relax your body and help you understand your disease a little better. First of all, I would like for you to be sitting in a way that you can feel very relaxed and very comfortable. You may wish to lie down. I will give you a few seconds to situate yourself in your chair or your bed so that your arms and legs can be relaxed and comfortable, and so that your back can be supported. Now I would like for you to pick a spot on the wall, comfortably look at it as I count downward from 10. I want you to continue to stare at the spot until your eyes become very heavy. 10, 9, 8, 7, 6, 5, 4, 3, 2, 1. Now gently close your eyes and ignore all of the sounds outside of the room. Just concentrate on my voice. Take some very deep breaths, breathing slowly and deeply, letting the air come in and go out. Each time you breathe out, let some of the tension leave your body. Breathe in, breathe out. Say to yourself, relax. Let that relaxed feeling spread all over your body.
>
> Now think for a moment about your feet. Let all of the tension flow out of your feet. Let the muscles become very loose and very smooth, very warm. Imagine the blood warming your feet, making them tingly. Think for a moment about your legs, your lower legs, your calves. Let all of the tension dissolve out of them, melting away, making them soft and smooth. Your upper legs, thighs, let them become very wam. Now, at the count of 3, I would like for you to be twice as relaxed as you are now. 1, 2, 3. In your minds eye, concentrate for a moment on your hips, letting them become very loose; muscles in your abdomen where

you may be storing a lot of tension, let that go. Let the blood flow through like the wind through the wheat, carrying good oxygen to all of your body. Continue to breathe regularly and deeply. Think for a second about the many muscles in your back. Mentally tell them to relax, to let go of all the tension and stress and anxiety they may be showing. Imagine the tension knots in your back and shoulders dissolving, melting, going away. The muscles in your neck relax, become very soft. Let them go. All up and down the back of your head and on the top of your head, let the tension free, flowing out. Allow the tiny muscles around your eyes to relax, around your jaw. Now, on the count of 3, I would like for you to make your entire body twice as relaxed as it is now. 1, 2, 3, twice as relaxed. That's right. Think for a moment about your arms, your hands, your fingers. See the blood flowing through them more and more, relaxing them. Now, while you are completely relaxed, I would like for you to stay very quiet and listen to some things about your disease.

Your doctor has told you that you are diabetic. Let's think a minute about what this means. As a matter of fact, we are not always sure about what causes a person to become diabetic, but we do know something about how your body reacts to this disease. First of all, it is important for you to realize that your body is a magnificent machine. It really is. We are like all machines; they need fuel to run properly. Now, just having sugar in the blood is not enough. It must enter the cells, all the muscles and tissues. Think of a toaster that is plugged in and not turned on. Or you may prefer to think of a car with a tank full of gas that is not running. Fuel is there; the toaster is plugged in; fuel's in the car, but it is not getting to the right parts to make the machine run. If you are a diabetic, that is how your body is functioning improperly. Picture your body with plenty of fuel rushing into your veins, but the fuel doesn't get to where it is needed, doesn't get into the cells of your muscles and tissues. It stays in your blood stream. Our bodies have a very special way of helping sugar get into the cells of the muscles and tissue, and this is how it takes place. We have a hormone that we manufacture within our body called insulin, which comes from the pancreas. Insulin helps the cells of your muscles and tissues take in the sugar; it helps them use it. It helps them store the sugar for future use. When you are a diabetic it means that your own insulin is not helping the sugar into the cells. Sometimes this may mean that you are not manufacturing enough insulin. Your doctor may be giving you extra insulin to help your body operate better. The insulin that you take in, that your doctor prescribes, acts like the insulin that you manufacture yourself.

Now I want you to imagine for a minute that insulin working in a way that makes sense to you, any way that makes sense to you. Imagine your cells with the insulin helping sugar from your blood into the muscles, into the tissues, into the cells. Imagine these things taking place any way you wish. Now imagine your pancreas. It can look any way that you want it to in your mind's eye. See it manufacturing more insulin. Imagine the insulin being released into your blood. You have been prescribed extra insulin from your doctor. See it coming into your body. Imagine it helping the sugar into the cells where the sugar is used to power each cell. See the sugar enter the cell as it leaves the blood stream.

Now I am gradually going to count to 3, and I would like for you to become alert whenever you are ready and continue whatever you have planned for today. Gently open your eyes when you are ready. 1, 2, 3.

Instructions for Drawing

"Now I am going to ask you to draw some of your images as they look to you. Do not worry about how well you can draw or how silly the images may seem.

These pictures help us to understand how you relate to your disease. I am going to ask you to draw three pictures, the first one being your pancreas (refer to the interview sheet for specific inquiry). Now, on this paper (separate page), draw how you see your beta cells working to produce insulin (refer to the interview sheet for specific inquiry). Now, draw how you see the insulin working (refer to the interview form for specific inquiry)."

Typically, we use typewriter paper with a pencil for drawing. However, crayons or paints have been used to increase response interest as well as to enhance details. After the person has finished the drawings, begin to inquire into each of the three areas, using the interview form as a guide. Each patient will have different concepts and a unique communication style. It is sometimes possible to allow the patient to rate his or her own drawing on many of the scales, since the ratings are made from both the interview and the drawings.

EVALUATING THE IMAGERY

Scores for the 16 dimensions of the Image-DB are derived from the visual and verbal information from the drawings and interview. The five-point evaluation for each dimension tends to be more nearly a 3-point scale (very low, average, and very high), with a score of "2" or "4" reserved for those whose images deviate only slightly from average.

As the person scoring the protocol gains experience from multiple examinations, the meaning of the five-point scale becomes quite clear. Specific guidance in scoring is presented below. The scoring system is structured so that high scores are related to the more favorable biological outcome. Figure 50 is an example of the Image-DB Scoring Sheet, and Figure 51 is an example of the Interview Record.

FIGURE 50

IMAGE-DB - Imagery Scoring Sheet

Name:
Age:
Medical Notes:

Circle the number you feel best describes the imagery, based on the information you have available.

PANCREAS

1. Vividness	1 very unclear	2 somewhat unclear	3 moderately vivid	4 quite vivid	5 maximally vivid
2. Activity	1 not at all active	2 somewhat active	3 moderately active	4 quite active	5 maximally active
3. Strength	1 quite weak	2 somewhat weak	3 moderately strong	4 quite strong	5 very strong
4. Size (relative to body)	1 very small	2 somewhat small	3 realistic proportion	4 somewhat large	5 very large

BETA CELLS (insulin-producing cells)

5. Vividness	1 very unclear	2 somewhat unclear	3 moderately vivid	4 quite vivid	5 maximally vivid

FIGURE 50 (*Continued*)
IMAGE-DB - Imagery Scoring Sheet

	1	2	3	4	5
6. Activity	not at all active	somewhat active	moderately active	quite active	very active
7. Numerosity	1 cell	2-5 cells	6-15 cells	16-30 cells	31 + cells
8. Size (relative to pancreas)	extremely small	moderately small	somewhat enlarged	moderately enlarged	greatly enlarged
9. Strength	quite weak	moderately weak	somewhat strong	quite strong	very strong

INSULIN (produced by own pancreas)

	1	2	3	4	5
10. Vividness	very unclear	somewhat unclear	moderately vivid	quite vivid	maximally vivid
11. Quantity (relative to amount.. of sugar in blood)	much more sugar	somewhat more sugar	about 50/50	somewhat less sugar	much less sugar
12. Effectiveness	not at all effective	moderately ineffective	moderately effective	quite effective	highly effective

FIGURE 50 (*Continued*)

IMAGE-DB - Imagery Scoring Sheet

GENERAL

	1	2	3	4	5
13. How Symbolistic is Visualization vs. How Concrete	very factual, concrete	moderately factual, concrete	mixed symbol-istic, factual	moderately symbolistic	highly symbolistic
14. Overall Strength of Imagery vs. Weakness	very weak	quite weak	moderate	quite strong	very sound, strong
15. Estimated Regularity of Positive Image	not imaging	infrequent	moderately regular	high level of consistency	extremely frequent
16. In your opinion, how is this type of imagery related to short-term disease management?	continued diabetes instability	some stabiliza-tion	considerable stabilization	eventual insulin decrease	rapid insulin decrease

IMAGE-DB - Interview Record

by Larry Stevens, Frank Lawlis, Jeanne Achterberg

PANCREAS

1. Describe how your pancreas looks in your mind's eye.

2. Do you see the pancreas functioning / active at all? If so, how? When?

3. How strong(tough) do you think your pancreas is?

4. About how big is your pancreas, relative to the size of your body?

BETA CELLS

5. Describe how your beta cells (your insulin-producing cells) in your pancreas look in your mind's eye. (Score on vividness, clarity, continuity of description.)

6. Do you see your beta cells moving in any way? If so, how? When? (Score on activity or potential activity.)

7. About how many beta cells do you see in your pancreas?

8. How big are your beta cells compared to the size of your pancreas as you see them in your mind's eye? (Score in comparison to approximate actual size.)

9. How strong (productive) are your beta cells? Are they able to produce as much insulin as they should?

INSULIN

10. Describe how your insulin works (what it does) as you see it in your mind's eye. (Score on vividness, clarity, continuity of description.)

11. How much of your own insulin do you see in your blood in comparison to sugar?

12. How good is your own insulin at doing what it is supposed to do?

MISCELLANEOUS RESPONSE (Not to be included as interview questions)

13. (Score on symbolism vs. realism.)

14. (Score on weak vs. strong.)

15. How many times a day do you think positively about (or image) your diabetes (pancreas, beta cells, or insulin)?

16. (Score imagery on basis of how you would predict it related to disease from a clinical standpoint, i.e., "5" would indicate it predicted excellent, very regular blood sugar maintenance and a gradual, progressive decrease in required exogenous insulin; "1" would predict very poor, extremely labile blood sugar levels and a progressive increase in required exogenous insulin.)

FIGURE 51

We will go into detail about how you should score each of the dimensions addressed on the Scoring Sheet. Here is a sample interview record with drawings (Figures 52, 53, and 54) and the scores assigned for this person (Figure 55). We present the sample here so that you can get some idea of the overall interaction and scoring process.

Interview Record for Sample Case

PANCREAS

1. Describe how your pancreas looks in your mind's eye.
   "Sorta bigger on one side then comes to a nose; pink; has little dots you can see that are islets."

2. Do you see the pancreas moving at all? If so, how? When?
   "Yes. Islets and beta cells are moving around. All the time they're moving. Moving in a shuffling way."

3. How strong (tough) do you think your pancreas is?
   "Pretty strong or tough. More than I thought."

4. About how big is your pancreas, relative to the size of your body?
   "Longer than a pencil."

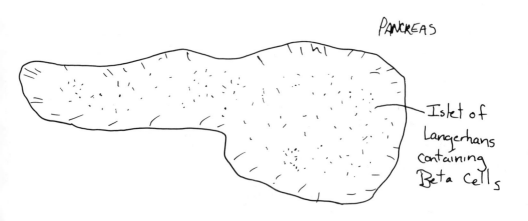

FIGURE 52. PANCREAS

5. Describe how your beta cells (your insulin-producing cells) in your pancreas look in your mind's eye. (Score on vividness, clarity, continuity of description).

   "They're round and dark on ends where insulin is; they have little staffs on them where they can boogie on down."

6. Do you see your beta cells moving in any way? If so, how? When? (Score on activity or potential activity.)

   "Yes, kinda dancing around on edge of pancreas like they're ready to go out and have a good time."

7. About how many beta cells do you see in your pancreas?

   "100."

8. How big are your beta cells compared to the size of your pancreas as you see them in your mind's eye? (Score in comparison to approximate actual size.)

   "Size of a printed music note."

9. How strong (productive) are your beta cells? Are they able to produce as much insulin as they should?

   "Really productive and strong. They're trying but not quite."

FIGURE 53 .   BETA CELLS

INSULIN

10. Describe how your insulin works (what it does) as you see it in your mind's eye. (Score on vividness, clarity, continuity of description.)

"Pancreas releases swinging insulin, then it goes through blood stream to all parts of body. Then it comes to the body cells and is trying to get inside. Glucose is there and then insulin says he's got a free pass and then they walk inside the body cells. And then energy is produced.

11. How much of your own insulin do you see in your blood in comparison to sugar?

"Lots!"

12. How good is your own insulin at doing what it is supposed to do?

"Really good!! High connections!"

FIGURE 54 . HOW INSULIN WORKS

216

MISCELLANEOUS RESPONSE

13. (Score on symbolism vs. realism.)

14. (Score on weak vs. strong.)

15. How many times a day do you think about (or image) your diabetes (pancreas, beta cells, or insulin)?

    "Diabetes, 5-10 times a day; pancreas, 5 or more times a day; beta cells, 5 times a day; insulin, 5 times a day."

16. (Score imagery on basis of how you would predict it related to disease from a clinical standpoint, i.e., "5" would indicate it predicted excellent, very regular blood sugar maintenance and a gradual, progressive decrease in required exogenous insulin; "1" would predict very poor, extremely labile blood sugar levels and a progressive increase in required exogenous insulin.)

FIGURE 55

IMAGE-DB- Imagery Scoring Sheet for Sample Case

Name:
Age:
Medical Notes:

Circle the number you feel best describes the imagery, based on the information you have available.

PANCREAS

1. Vividness	1 very unclear	2 somewhat unclear	3 moderately vivid	(4) quite vivid	5 maximally vivid
2. Activity	1 not at all active	2 somewhat active	3 moderately active	(4) quite active	5 maximally active
3. Strength	1 quite weak	2 somewhat weak	(3) moderately strong	4 quite strong	5 very strong
4. Size (relative to body)	1 very small	(2) somewhat small	3 realistic proportion	4 somewhat large	5 very large

BETA CELLS (insulin-producing cells)

5. Vividness	1 very unclear	2 somewhat unclear	3 moderately vivid	(4) quite vivid	5 maximally vivid

FIGURE 55 (*Continued*)

IMAGE-DB- Imagery Scoring Sheet for Sample Case

	1	2	3	4	5
6. Activity	not at all active	somewhat active	moderately active	quite active	**⑤** very active
7. Numerosity	1 cell	2-5 cells	6-15 cells	16-30 cells	**⑤** 31 + cells
8. Size (relative to pancreas)	extremely small	moderately small	somewhat enlarged	**④** moderately enlarged	5 greatly enlarged
9. Strength	quite weak	moderately weak	somewhat strong	**④** quite strong	5 very strong

INSULIN (produced by own pancreas)

	1	2	3	4	5
10. Vividness	very unclear	somewhat unclear	moderately vivid	quite vivid	**⑤** maximally vivid
11. Quantity (relative to amount of sugar in blood) . .	much more sugar	somewhat more sugar	about 50/50	somewhat less sugar	**⑤** much less sugar
12. Effectiveness	not at all effective	moderately ineffective	moderately effective	quite effective	**⑤** highly effective

FIGURE 55 (*Continued*)

IMAGE-DB- Imagery Scoring Sheet for Sample Case

GENERAL

	1	2	3	4	5
13. How Symbolistic is Visualization vs. How Concrete	very factual, concrete	moderately factual, concrete	mixed symbolistic, factual	moderately symbolistic	(5) highly symbolistic
14. Overall Strength of Imagery vs. Weakness	very weak	quite weak	moderate	(4) quite strong	very sound, strong
15. Estimated Regularity of Positive Image	not imaging	infrequent	moderately regular	high level of consistency	(5) extremely frequent
16. In your opinion, how is this type of imagery related to short-term disease management?	continued diabetes instability	some stabilization	considerable stabilization	(4) eventual insulin decrease	rapid insulin decrease

CHAPTER 11

DISEASE DIMENSIONS AND CASE EXAMPLES

The next section presents general descriptions of the dimensions.

1. Vividness of the pancreas.

Vividness, as used on several of these dimensions, relates to the clarity with which the person describes the entity in question. Vividness is also determined by the specificity or detail supplied. Assign a "3" on this scale if the person gives a general description of shape with two additional features such as color, size, temperature. Give a high score if the person expresses intricate details of appearance and a low score if the description of the pancreas is amorphous, colorless, nondescript.

Figure 56 shows a good example of a "5" rating for this dimension. The specificity of the space ship was very clear to the examiner. The patient described many details and features of the space ship:

The pancreas is a circle like a totally self-contained space station with beta cells. The beta cells are like small asteroids leaving for distribution. It is suspended in space with the only movement being the beta cells leaving. It is very stable, very efficient, and does a great job. The beta cells, the mini space ships, are carrying beta cells, are often used in the blood stream to get to the rest of the body. They are continuous beta cells as long as I imagine them, infinite. They are small, like the size of charcoal relative to the size of space stations. They are perfect, a totally good beta cell. The other space stations (tissues) receive energy (insulin). I have not yet developed fantasy of what insulin does to the tissue. There is a steady stream, doing its job 100%. I feel good doing this.

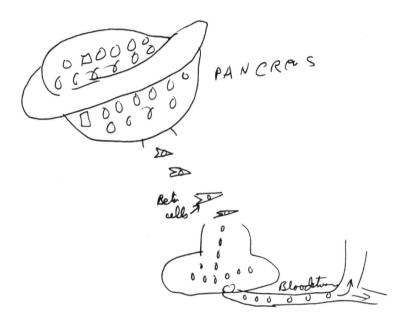

FIGURE 56. HIGH RATING ON VIVIDNESS OF THE PANCREAS

Figure 57, however, received a low rating due to its lack of clarity and detail:

The pancreas is sitting there not doing anything, not moving. It is dead. It is about 2 inches big. The beta cells are like Pac-Man, eating up sugar. They are moving around all the time in the blood stream, like they were shot from a machine. They are microscopic and are rated a zero as to productiveness. My insulin does not work. None of my insulin is in the blood stream.

FIGURE 57. LOW RATING ON VIVIDNESS OF THE PANCREAS

2. Activity (function) of the pancreas.

Score this dimension based upon the person's general description of the drawing and/or from his or her answers to direct questioning as to how active or functional the pancreas is perceived to be at the time of testing. (100% active or functioning would, of course, be given a "5," with relatively lower scores for decreasing percentages.)

Figure 56 above is also a good example of a high rating for this dimension. Examiners consistently rated it a "5" because of the definitive action of the pancreas, inferring a vital, moving, and directive functioning.

The next drawing, Figure 58, was rated very low ("1") because of the inferred "deadness" quality. As the client aptly put it, "Maybe Jesus could raise it (the pancreas) from the dead."

The pancreas is behind the stomach; I cannot describe the shape. All of the cells are inside it, like little people on an island. It is not moving. It just sits there. It is not hitting on all 4 now, it is eroded. Maybe Jesus can raise it from the dead. It is 6-8 inches oblong shape. The beta cells are little round things with jagged edges. The beta cells are different colors from the delta. They are not moving, but the vessels are. There are thousands or millions. They are microscopic. They are strong because there is strength in numbers. The insulin is like a gate and insulin opens it. I cannot draw it, I am too frustrated!

FIGURE 58. LOW RATING ON ACTIVITY OF THE PANCREAS

3. Strength of the pancreas.

Strength is not only highly related to the description of activity, but also the expression of the potential of the pancreas to create insulin.

Because of the imaged strength within the space ship, the drawing in Figure 56 above was rated high on this dimension. A general rule for scoring of strength is to consider the inferred strength of the symbol itself, the metaphorical quality inherent in such a symbol. In this case, the space ship can be viewed as a mighty, modern force.

4. Size of the pancreas.

The size of the pancreas is judged primarily from the drawing, but can be solicited from the patient. The pancreas is approximately the same size as the stomach, and the typical response is that the pancreas is the size of a fist or potato. When scoring the drawing, note the person's image of the size of the pancreas relative to body size. The average response (3) would be a response that would be appropriate and be realistically proportionate to the rest of the body. If the pancreas is large relative to body size, a higher score would result.

The drawing in Figure 59 was rated in the lowest level for this dimension because of the small, weak symbol chosen (a gizzard). The vastness of the space ship in Figure 56 would imply, on the other hand, a large organ and would receive a high score.

The pancreas looks like a half moon, a gizzard of a chicken.
It is not moving, not very tough, very soft, about the size of a
half dollar. The beta cells are like beans, moving, flowing
along the blood vessels. There are 30-50 of them, half the size
of a green pea, strong, barely moving. I don't have an image of
insulin because I do not have any.

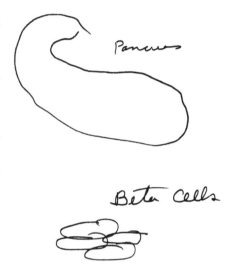

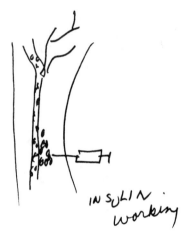

FIGURE 59. LOW RATING ON SIZE OF THE PANCREAS

5. *Vividness of the beta cells.*

Vividness of the beta cells relates to the specificity
and clarity with which the patient perceives the beta cells.
Again, as used in vividness of the pancreas, when the patient
can be very specific, utilizing at least two of the sensory
features that might be related and perhaps include personality
features or characteristics, give an average rating of 3. Five
or more features voluntarily included so as to characterize the
percept with great, explicit understanding would give the
dimension a high rating of 5. A vague, unclear picture would
give a very low rating scale score of 1.

Figure 60 below is an example of a low score on this dimension:

The pancreas is oblong shape, probably pink. It is not moving, not very tough or strong, and the size of a hot dog. *The beta cells are probably small and dark. There are about 20, about the size of a pencil lead and do not produce a lot. They do pulsate.* The insulin is trapped in my pancreas and doesn't get out to burn up much sugar. My insulin is not very good, very little. Much of the sugar goes out in the kidneys.

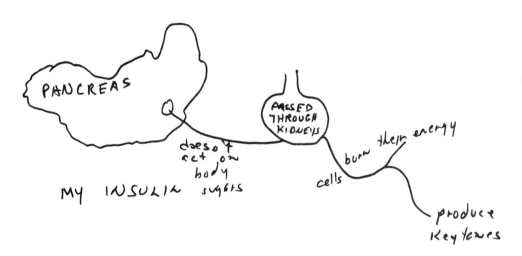

FIGURE 60. LOW RATING ON VIVIDNESS OF BETA CELLS

Remember Figure 56, on the other hand. Here is how the person described the beta cells: "The beta cells, the mini space ships, are carrying the beta cells, are often used in the blood stream to get to the rest of the body. They are continuous beta cells as long as I imagine them, infinite. They are small, like the size of charcoal relative to the size of space stations. They are perfect, a totally good beta cell." Here, the specificity exemplifies a high score on this dimension.

6. Activity of the beta cells.

The activity of the beta cells score is typically derived from the direct question to the patient. By asking how active the beta cells appear to be at the present time (active, moderately active, or very active), a general score can be derived at once.

The lack of specificity in Figure 60 above, though, would call for the assignment of a low score. The patient describes the cells as "probably small" with relatively inexact dimensions, i.e., "like pencil lead, probably dark." The examiner is given little with which the image can be understood.

The drawing in Figure 61 exemplifies a high activity level of beta cells. Although it is described through images of sound, the energy is definitely high.

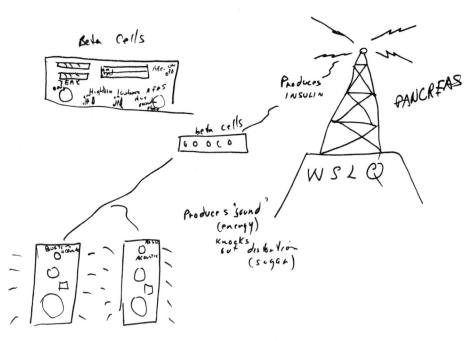

FIGURE 61. HIGH RATING ON ACTIVITY OF BETA CELLS

The pancreas looks like a huge radio transmitter, pouring out the music (insulin). It does not move, it just pours out energy. It's pretty strong, about 4-5 inches. *The beta cells are like a "TEAK" receiver, like a component stereo, not moving. There are about 10,000 and less than 1/16 of an inch. They are pretty strong and can handle a lot.* The pancreas produces the insulin and, like a receiver, the insulin takes it into the muscles, like speakers, produce energy.

7. Numerosity of the beta cells.

The number of the cells that the patient images are categorized: If one or no cells, the scale score is "1" (very low); 6 to 15 cells constitute an average rating; and 31 or more cells constitute a superior rating.

8. Size of beta cells.

As in the rating for the size of the pancreas being proportioned to the rest of the body, the size of the beta cells are judged as related to the size of the pancreas. More often than not, this rating is derived from the interview in which the patient is asked directly how large he or she perceives the beta cells to be. Inasmuch as the patient is asked to focus upon these particular cells, the typical drawing has the beta cells somewhat enlarged (approximately 1/10th to 1/15th the size of the pancreas). If the beta cells are extremely small or non-existent, the lower scores are obtained; however, if the cells are 1/2 to the same size of the pancreas, the larger scores are obtained.

The microscopic cells described in Figure 58 would be given a low score: "There are thousands or millions. They are microscopic." Figure 56 describes the beta cells as beans and the pancreas as the size of a half-dollar. This would be given the relatively high rating of "4."

229

9. *Strength of the beta cells.*

This scale score is typically obtained from the questions administered directly. The patient is asked to estimate how strong the beta cells are within his or her body (very weak, somewhat strong, or very strong). Qualifications and his or her response would typify the immediate scores.

In the drawing presented in Figure 57, the patient used "Pac-Man" as the imagery. This might be considered an aggressive symbol for some people. However, when asked, the patient rated the strength as a "zero." Consequently, the rating for the scale was "1." The patient whose drawing was presented in Figure 61 described his beta cells as "pretty strong and can handle a lot," justifying a high rating for beta cell strength.

10. *Vividness of the insulin.*

Vividness of the insulin incorporates the same criteria as in scales 1 and 5. If the patient can perceive the insulin component in such a way as to communicate it clearly to the examiner, the average score of "3" is usually indicated. If 5 or more features are voluntarily given, a high score is indicated. Vague, unclear responses would give the lower scores.

The patient whose drawing was presented in Figure 57 did not have a clear image or symbol of his insulin: "My insulin does not work. None of my insulin is in the blood stream." A score of "1" was assigned.

In the next drawing, Figure 62, the rating of "4" was assigned for the additional properties of the key image. Efforts to give the image many features would result in higher scores. For example, several features given to the insulin would warrant a "5" rating.

230

FIGURE 62. GOOD RATING ON VIVIDNESS OF INSULIN

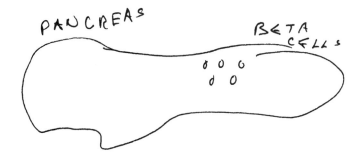

The pancreas is a blob of cells, fat at one end, long, like a key, but for me it is like a dead piece of meat. It is very sensitive in the internal layers to infection. It is about the size of a fist. The beta cells are circular, the size of pinheads with a black nucleus and fluid. They do move back and forth with the fluid, like amoeba. They number in the thousands, about the size of pinheads or smaller, but not very productive at all. *The insulin is the key that opens the door to allow sugar to go into the tissues, but it is not open.* I would hope that my insulin does what it is supposed to do.

FIGURE 62 (*Continued*)

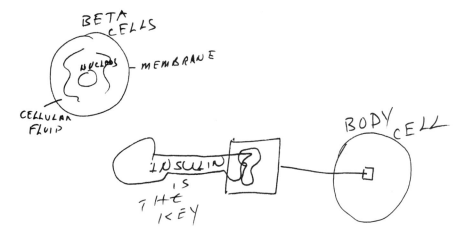

11. *Quantity of insulin.*

This factor is relative to the amount of sugar in the blood stream. An average score is the condition in which there is the same amount of insulin as there is sugar. If there is more insulin than sugar in the blood stream, the elevated scores are obtained, whereas if there is more sugar than insulin, the lower scores are obtained.

12. *Effectiveness of the insulin.*

This score can be obtained directly from the interview. In the situation in which the patient perceives the insulin to be at least moderately effective in its performance, an average score of "3" is assigned. The criterion for a "5" would be met when the patient perceives the insulin as being very effective, whereas the low score would indicate the perception that the insulin has little or no effect at all.

Diabetics have a difficult time imagining their insulin as very effective in the present tense when they are dependent upon synthetic or artificial sources. The patient whose drawing was presented in Figure 57 said: "My insulin does not work. None of my insulin is in the blood stream." Another said: "I don't have an image of insulin because I do not have any."

The drawing in Figure 61 would receive a high rating on insulin effectiveness: "The pancreas produces insulin and, like a receiver, the insulin takes it into the muscles, which like speakers produce energy."

13. *Symbolization versus realism.*

The criterion for the average score for this particular scale is one in which some symbolization of at least one of the components (insulin, pancreas, beta cells) is noted. Symbolization is present when the person ascribes some feature that is not anatomical in its nature. For example, if beta cells are described as happy faces, devils, or having horns or legs, this would necessarily imply some symbolization. Very high scores (5) would have the total image as being symbolic in nature (angels, vikings, and rivers, etc.). Very factual or anatomical pictures would be scored in the low range (1-2).

14. *Overall strength of imagery.*

The overall strength of the imagery is rated on the basis of the integration of all of the components. The typical response is one where the components (pancreas, beta cells, and insulin) have functions that are, at best, weakly associated. A very strong imagery would be one in which there is a definite connection between these components, often relating to each other in anthropomorphic terms. Elaboration is often made on how they function with regard to the other parts of the body and mind, but also very specific mechanics of off-and-on monitoring devices may be given. Very weak scores reflect nonintegration and inconsistencies in relating to the imagery.

The cases involving the space ship and the radio transmitter show integration of the images. They are coherent and planful and imply positive outcome. The drawing of Figure 58, as shown on page 224, clearly does not have any overall conceptual strength.

15. *Overall regularity of the positive image.*

The overall regularity score is based upon how frequently the images are recalled each day. The score is typically taken directly from the question concerning how frequently or regularly components are perceived as operating in a positive way. It is important to emphasize the positive here. If the system is imaged as breaking down often, this would not be considered to be regular positive imaging. The scores typically relate to a continuum of not using positive imagery at all, moderately, and frequently.

16. Clinical impressions.

This scale score is primarily an overall rating of how well it is felt the patient will be doing in the future in terms of personality and motivational factors, as well as physical health. The typical response is one in which some stabilization of the disease process is anticipated, whereas extremely positive anticipation of a healthy lifestyle would be a high rating of "5." A postulated decline in status would be a "1."

CHAPTER 12

STANDARDIZATION AND RESEARCH WITH THE TECHNIQUE

In order to determine the overall score, the examiner must combine the ratings of each of the 16 dimensions in two basic steps:

1) The summation of the raw ratings into the total raw score;

2) The transformation of the raw score into the standard score (sten).

The Image-DB scoring sheet provides space for these computations.

The sum of the ratings is simply the arithmetic sum of the 16 scores. In order to compare the meaning of the total summed score in relationship to an overall distribution, the sum is converted into standard scores ranging from one to ten (sten). The conversion is made by locating in Table 21 the summed ratings in the left column and then reading directly across to find the associated sten score.

Meaning of Sten

As in the Image-CA, the distribution of the overall scores is based upon a normal distribution. In the development of this test, the mean was set at 5.5 with a standard deviation of 2.0. In terms of variance, this typically means that the score of 5 to 6 would fall in the average range with 3 to 4 and 7 to 8 being slightly below or above average, and the extreme two scores at either end would indicate extreme deviation.

Table 21

CONVERSION OF RAW SCORES TO STENS *

Raw Scores	Stens	
0-21	1	Very Low
22-27	2	
28-33	3	Lower Than
34-39	4	Average
40-45	5	Average
46-51	6	
52-57	7	Greater Than
58-63	8	Average
64-71	9	Very High
72-	10	

*The standardization sample consisted of 45 Type I diabetic patients (age range 14-65 years).

Missing or Nonapplicable Ratings

There are times when some dimensions are either inappropriate or missing. For example, dimension 16 (clinical evaluation) becomes an extremely important criterion as the examiner gains experience. However, when the initial cases are learning sessions, or when the ratings constitute a research project, the 16th dimension could be left out. In such cases, consult Table 22 and insert the mean for the particular dimension. For example, the mean of Clinical Evaluation Scale 16 is 2.6. This value would be inserted into that particular sum and added to the rest of the ratings.

Table 22

LIST OF MEANS AND STANDARD DEVIATIONS

Var ID #	Variable Name	Mean	Standard Deviation
1	VP	3.17	.99
2	AP	2.47	1.48
3	SP	2.94	1.22
4	SP	2.88	.76
5	VB	3.20	.94
6	AB	2.76	1.47
7	No.	4.38	1.15
8	Size	2.41	1.47
9	Stren	2.55	1.33
10	VI	3.38	1.04
11	Quan	2.35	1.57
12	Effect	2.76	1.53
13	Sym	2.64	1.53
14	Over	3.11	1.12
15	Reg	3.94	1.36
16	Clin	2.61	1.41
17	Total	46.00	12.36

RESEARCH WITH THE TECHNIQUE

Reliability

Reliabilities and validities are based on a sample of 72 cases. Since this test is a rating scale, an interreliability measure is considered of paramount importance. Based on two independent scores, the overall reliability in two separate samples yielded interrater reliability coefficients of .82 and .94, respectively. Internal reliability yielded a coefficient of .97 (alpha). Internal correlations of the respective dimensions to the total score are furnished in Table 23.

Table 23

CORRELATIONS OF SCALES WITH TOTAL SCORE

Scale		Correlation
1	VP	.50
2	AP	.33
3	SP	.33
4	SP	.47
5	VB	.74
6	AB	.21
7	No.	.40
8	Size	.16
9	Stren	.82
10	Vi	.77
11	Quan	.82
12	Effect	.85
13	Sym	.70
14	Over	.84
15	Reg	.47
16	Clin	.90

Validity

It is desirable to demonstrate that the Image-DB relates both to quality of life and to glucose levels. However, only the latter could be ascertained within this research. Larry Stevens (1983) in his dissertation with diabetes found that the Image-DB correlated significantly with blood glucose levels (—.53). The study by Stevens was based upon the responses of 45 outpatient, insulin-dependent diabetics. He assigned 15 patients to each of three groups: a stress management approach, an interpersonal relationship enhancement approach, and a no-treatment group. Results of metabolic improvements for the treatment groups in urine glucose and blood glucose magnitudes were evident, with the stress management group having better readings at long-term follow up. Individual correlations across groups for physiological co-variance and imagery scores were such that the use of the Image-DB could be justified as a dependent measure of diabetic improvements. Other clinical studies of individuals have shown some basis for interpreting the findings in meaningful ways for overall adjustment to diabetes (Achterberg & Lawlis, 1980; Kershaw, 1979).

REFERENCES
PART III
IMAGE-DB

Achterberg, J., & Lawlis, G. F. *Bridges of the bodymind: Behavioral approaches to health care.* Champaign, Ill.: Institute for Personality and Ability Testing, 1980.

Benton, P. C. The emotional aspects of diabetes mellitus. *Journal of the Oklahoma Medical Association*, 1953, *46*, 11.

Bradley, C. Life events and the control of diabetes mellitus. *Journal of Psychosomatic Research*, 1976, *23*, 159-162.

Cannon, W. B., Shohl, A. T., & Wright, W. W. Emotional glycosuria. *American Journal of Physiology*, 1911, *29*, 280.

Chase, H. P., & Jackson, G. G. Stress and sugar control in children with insulin-dependent diabetes mellitus. *The Journal of Pediatrics*, 1981, *98*(6), 1011-1013.

Daniels, G. E. Emotional and instinctual factors in diabetes mellitus. *Psychoanalytic Quarterly*, 1936, *5*, 513.

Dunbar, F. *Psychosomatic Diagnosis.* New York: Paul B Hoeber, Inc., 1943.

Folin, O., Denis, W., & Smillie, W. G. Some observations on emotional glycosuria in man. *Journal of Biological Chemistry*, 1914, *17*, 519.

Grant, I., Kyle, G. C., Teichman, A., & Mendels, J. Recent life events and diabetes in adults. *Psychosomatic Medicine*, 1974, *36*(2), 121-128.

Hinkle, L. E., Conger, G. B., & Wolf, S. Studies on diabetes mellitus: The relation of stressful life situations to the concentration of ketone bodies in the blood of diabetic and non-diabetic humans. *Journal of Clinical Investigation*, 1950, *29*, 754-769.

Hinkle, L. E., Evans, F., & Wolf. S. Studies in diabetes mellitus, III: Life history of three persons with labile diabetes and relation of significant experiences in their lives to the onset and course of the disease. *Psychosomatic Medicine*, 1951, *13*, 160-183.

Hinkle, L. E., & Wolf, S. A summary of experimental evidence relating life stress to diabetes mellitus. *Journal of the Mount Sinai Hospital*, 1952, *19*(4), 537-570.

Holmes, T. H., & Rahe, R. H. The social readjustment rating scale. *Journal of Psychosomatic Research*, 1967, *11*, 213-218.

Hong, M., & Homes, T. H. Transient diabetes mellitus associated with culture change. *Archives of General Psychiatry*, 1973, *29*, 683-687.

Kershaw, C. J. Effects of visual imagery and relaxation on the psychophysiology of diabetic functioning (Doctoral dissertation, East Texas State University). *Dissertation Abstracts International*, 1979, *40* (2-B), 895-896.

Menninger, W. C. Psychological factors in the etiology of diabetes mellitus. *Journal of Nervous and Mental Disorders*, 1935, *81*, 1.

Meyer, A., Bollmeyer, L. N., & Alexander, F. Correlations between emotions and carbohydrate metabolism in two cases of diabetes mellitus. *Psychosomatic Medicine*, 1945, *7*, 335.

Rosen, H., & Lidz, T. Emotional factors in the precipitation of recurrent diabetic acidosis. *Psychosomatic Medicine*, 1949, *11*, 211.

Simon, N. M., & Mirsky, S. The roles of emotional stress and diet in the etiology of diabetes mellitus. *Quarterly Bulletin of Northwestern University Medical School*, 1953, *27*, 2.

Slawson, P. F., Flynn, W. R., & Kollar, E. J. Psychological factors associated with the onset of diabetes mellitus. *Journal of the American Medical Association*, 1963, *185*(3), 166-170.

Stevens, L. *An intervention study of imagery with diabetes mellitus.* Unpublished doctoral dissertation, North Texas State University, 1983.

Vandenbergh, R. L., Sussman, K. E., & Titus, C. C. Effects of hypnotically induced acute emotional stress on carbohydrate and lipid metabolism in patients with diabetes mellitus. *Psychosomatic Medicine*, 1966, *28*(4), 382-390.

Vandenbergh, R. L., Sussman, K. E., & Vaughan, G. D. Effects of combined physical-anticipatory stress on carbohydrate-lipid metabolism in patients with diabetes mellitus. *Psychosomatics*, 1967, *8*, 16-19.

AUTHOR INDEX

SUBJECT INDEX